REWARD

REWARD

Starter

Practice Book

Diana Pye
Simon Greenall

D1612001

MACMILLAN
HEINEMANN
English Language Teaching

VOCABULARY

1 Find the words in Lesson 1 of your Student's Book.

say   repeat   listen   complete   read   punctuate
ask   write   match   find

2 Match the words with the pictures.

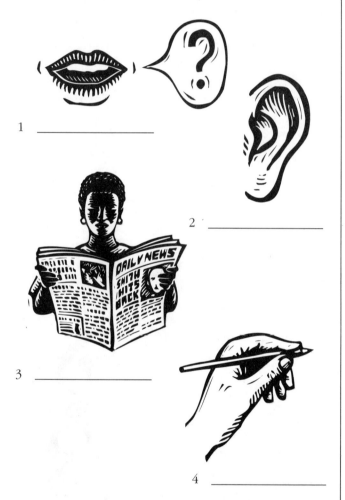

1 _____

2 _____

3 _____

4 _____

3 Find 8 classroom words from Lesson 1.

L	I	S	T	E	N
W	F	I	N	D	M
R	T	S	A	Y	A
I	A	S	K	D	T
T	R	E	A	D	C
E	D	P	S	A	H
R	E	P	E	A	T

4 Put the letters in order. Write words from Lesson 1.

esapel: *please*

ruoy: _____   nda: _____

hatw: _____   ohlle: _____

mean: _____   ooeygbd: _____

FUNCTIONS

1 Punctuate and write the sentences.

what'syourname
   What's your name?

1 i'mmaria

   _____

2 hellomariai'mfrank

   _____

3 andwhat'syourname

   _____

4 myname'sjohn

   _____

2 Write the complete form.

What's your name? = *What is your name?*

My name's Diana. = _____

I'm Petra. = _____

2

SOUNDS

1 🔊 Listen and repeat.

hello   name   what's   please   goodbye   your
listen   read   write   repeat

2 🔊 Listen again and write.

1 syllable	2 syllables
o	o o
name	*he llo*
_____	_____
_____	_____
_____	_____
_____	_____
_____	_____
_____	_____

LISTENING AND WRITING

1 🔊 Listen and number.

I'm Maria.   ☐

Goodbye.   ☐

Hello, Petra.   ☐

What's your name, please?   ☐

And what's your name?   ☐

I'm Petra.   ☐

2 🔊 Listen and match the conversations with the pictures.

3 Read and complete.

1   Hello. _____ name?

2   _____ Steve. And what's

    _____?

3   _____ Katy.

4 🔊 Listen to Conversation 1 again and check.

WRITING

1 Write the conversation for the other picture.

JANE _____

ANNA _____

JANE _____

2 🔊 Listen to Conversation 2 again and check.

3 Answer the question for you.

What's your name?

_____ _____

4 Write the conversation.

A STUDENT _____

YOU _____

A STUDENT _____

A ☐   **B** ☐

3

2 | *I'm a student*

VOCABULARY

1 Write 8 jobs from Lesson 2.

_____
_____
_____
_____
_____
_____
_____
_____

2 Match the jobs with the pictures.

1 *student*_____   2 _____

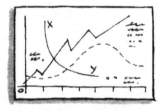

3 _____   4 _____

5 _____   6 _____

7 _____   8 _____

3 Complete and write words from Lessons 1 and 2.

1 _ h _ t   6 y _ _ r
2 _ _ t _ _ ss   7 _ _ ll _
3 _ oo _ b y _   8 n _ m _
4 w _ _ _ er   9 s _ _ g _ _
5 _ o _   10 j _ _ r n _ l _ _ t

GRAMMAR

1 Put in order and write the sentences.

1 job   is   your   what?
_____

2 am   engineer   I   an
_____

3 name   is   my   Sarah
_____

4 name   what   your   is?
_____

5 secretary   am   a   I
_____

2 Write *a* or *an*.

I'm _*a*_ teacher.
1 I'm ___ student.
2 Are you ___ engineer?
3 You're ___ doctor!
4 I'm ___ actress.
5 Are you ___ waiter?
6 I'm ___ actor.

3 Complete the questions.

1 _____ is your name?
2 _____ is your job?

4 Answer the questions for you.

1 _____
2 _____

SOUNDS

1 Read and match.

teacher   engineer   doctor   actress   journalist
singer

o   o   o   o   o

tea   cher

2 🔊 Listen and check. Say the words.

3 🔊 Listen and look.

PETE   What's your name?
    o   o   O

SALLY   My name's Sally.
    o   o   O

PETE   I'm Pete.
    o   O

SALLY   What's your job?
    o   o   O

PETE   I'm a waiter.
    o   o   O

4 🔊 Listen again and repeat.

LISTENING AND SPEAKING

1 🔊 Listen and complete Conversations 1 and 2.

Conversation 1
Hello, I'm Bill. What's your name?
Hello, Bill. I'm Pat.
What's your job, Pat?
I'm _____

Conversation 2
Hello, _____ Cathy. What's _____

_____

Hello, Cathy. _____ Eric.
What's _____ _____ Eric?
_____ ____ _____

2 🔊 Listen again and check.

3 🔊 Look at the picture. Listen and answer for you.

1 Hello. I'm John. What's your name?

_____

2 And what's your job?

_____

WRITING

Look at the questions in *Listening and speaking* activity 3. Write the answers.

5

3 | *How are you?*

VOCABULARY

1 **Put the numbers in order.**

two   ten   one   six   three   zero   five   nine   seven   four   eight

zero _____

_____

_____

2 **Complete the puzzles with numbers.**

3 **Correct the spelling.**

plese ___*please*___

goodby _____

helo _____

thanck you _____

foor _____

eigt _____

telefone _____

SOUNDS

1 **Say.**

/aɪ/: nine   fine   five   I'm   my   write

🔲 Listen and repeat.

2 🔲 **Listen and write.**

six _____   _____

_____   _____

_____   _____

_____   _____

_____   _____

🔲 Listen again and repeat.

3 🔲 **Listen and look.**

1   I'm a<u>n a</u>ctor.

2   I'<u>m E</u>ric.

3   Ho<u>w a</u>re you?

4   pho<u>ne n</u>umber

4 🔲 Listen again and repeat.

GRAMMAR

1 **Punctuate and write the sentences.**

1   hellohowareyou

_____

2   hellojohnhowareyou

_____

3   hellotonyi'mverywellthankshowareyou

_____

4   i'mfinethanks

_____

5   i'mverywellthankyou

_____

6   what'syourphonenumber

_____

6

2 Write the long forms.

1 I'm fine. = *I am fine.*

2 What's your name? = _____
   _____

3 I'm a waiter = _____
   _____

4 My name's Diana. = _____
   _____

5 I'm very well, thanks. = _____
   _____

6 What's your phone number? = _____
   _____

3 Match question and answer.

1 What's your name?   a I'm fine, thanks.
2 What's your phone number? b I'm Sarah.
3 How are you?   c I'm a singer.
4 What's your job?   d 01749 603 521.

LISTENING AND SPEAKING

1 Say the phone numbers.

01981 428 969   01918 762 896   01438 650 329
596 227 851   01876 432 549   01246 993 682

📼 Listen and check.

2 📼 Listen and correct the phone numbers.

1 Sarah: 01689 432 873
              7   9

2 Jeanne: 01293 906 625

3 Tom: 01292 598 829

4 Ben: 01583 731 496

3 📼 Listen again and check.

4 📼 Listen and write the telephone numbers.

Conversation 1

JOHN   Hello, Emma. How are you?
EMMA   I'm fine. What's your phone number, John?
JOHN   _____

Conversation 2

MEG   Hello. I'm Meg. I'm a student. What's your name?
JIM   Hello, Meg. I'm Jim. I'm a student, too.
MEG   What's your phone number?
JIM   _____

Are you James Bond?

VOCABULARY AND SOUNDS

1 🔊 Listen and repeat.

ABCDE FGHIJ HIJKL LMNOP PQRST
UVWXYZ

2 Spell.

how   what   yes   spell   read   John   Anna

🔊 Listen and check.

3 🔊 Listen and write.

1 *NAME*
2 W _ _ _
3 P _ _ _ _ _
4 H _ _ _ _
5 S _ _ _ _
6 A _ _

🔊 Listen again and check.

4 🔊 Listen and repeat.

1 Hello. What's your name, please?
2 How do you spell that?
3 Are you Michael?
4 Goodbye, Michael.

GRAMMAR

1 Complete with (?) or (.) .

Yes, I am_.

1 What's your name_
2 My name's Pete_
3 How do you spell your name_
4 No, I'm not_
5 Are you Steve_
6 Read and complete_

2 Put the words in 2 groups.

is name are number am job

Nouns	Verbs
name	_____
_____	_____
_____	_____

3 Write the questions.

1 _____
   I'm Maria.
2 _____
   No, I'm not. I'm John.
3 _____
   P-H-I-L-I-P.
4 _____
   Yes, I am.
5 _____
   I'm a secretary.
6 _____
   I'm fine, thanks.

4 Correct the sentences.

1 My name Janet.

   _____

2 How are you spell that?

   _____

3 I'm teacher.

   _____

4 What your job?

   _____

5 I very well, thank you.

   _____

6 How you are?

   _____

READING AND LISTENING

1 Read and complete.

(1) _____

Yes, I am. Are you Jane?

(2) _____

What's your name?

(3) _____

What's your job?

(4) _____

a My name's Helen.
b No, I'm not.
c I'm a doctor.
d Are you Philip?

🔈 Listen and check.

2 🔈 Listen and correct.

A Are you an actor?

B Yes, I am. And you, are you a waitress?

A No, I'm not. I'm a teacher.

🔈 Listen again and check.

3 Read and complete.

no   please   hello   please   yes   no   thank you
hello

A _____ . Are you Steve?

B _____ , I'm not. I'm Michael.

A And what's your name, _____?

C My name's Naomi.

A _____ .

🔈 Listen and check.

WRITING

1 Write sentences.

1 What _____
_____

2 My _____
_____

3 How _____
_____

4 Are _____
_____

5 I'm _____
_____

2 Answer questions about yourself.

Hello. Are you Mary?

_____

What's your name?

_____

How do you spell that?

_____

How are you?

_____

What's your job?

_____

What's your phone number?

_____

Goodbye.

5 | *She's Russian*

SOUNDS

1 Say and match.

Brazil England Germany India Italy Japan Mexico Sweden Thailand Turkey

O o *England* _____

_____

o O _____

_____

O o o _____

_____

🔲 Listen and check.

2 🔲 Listen again and repeat.

3 🔲 Listen and look.

1 What's your nationality?
   o   o   O

2 I'm British.
   o   O

3 What's your name?
   o   o   O

4 My name's Anna.
   o   o   O

5 She's a teacher.
   o o O

6 Where's Sema from?
   o   O   o

7 He's from Turkey.
   o   o   O

4 🔲 Listen again and repeat.

VOCABULARY AND SPEAKING

1 Complete.

Country	Nationality
Turkey	*Turkish*
The United States	_____
Britain	_____
Japan	_____
Italy	_____
France	_____
Korea	_____
China	_____
Russia	_____
Switzerland	_____

2 Say and write.

Jane is British.
She's from Britain.

1 Sema is Turkish.

_____

_____

2 Anna is Italian.

_____

_____

3 I'm English.

_____

_____

4 Newton is Brazilian.

_____

_____

5 You're American.

_____

_____

3 Write the nationality.

She's from Barcelona in Spain.

She's Spanish.

1 He's from Tokyo in Japan.

_____

2 He's from Istanbul in Turkey.

_____

3 She's from the United States of America.

_____

4 He's from Moscow.

_____

5 She's from France.

_____

GRAMMAR

1 Match.

are   is   am

Pronoun	Verb
I	_____
you	_____
he	_____
she	_____

2 Complete with a word from activity 1.

1 I _____ British.

2 He _____ French.

3 She _____ Japanese.

4 You _____ Argentinian.

3 Write sentences.

1 Where's he from?

(Brazil) _____

2 Where's she from?

(Thailand) _____

3 Where are you from?

(?) _____

4 Complete with *a/an* or -.

1 I'm _____ waiter.

2 She's _____ German.

3 He's from _____ Brazil.

4 You're _____ actor!

LISTENING AND SPEAKING

1 Put in order.

a   Yes, I am. I'm from London.

b   Hello, Sammy. My name's Janet.

c   No, I'm from Canada. And you? Are you British?

d   Hello. I'm Sammy.

e   Are you American, Janet?

2 🔲 Listen and check.

3 🔲 Listen and answer the questions for you.

WRITING

🔲 Listen to the questions in *Listening and speaking* activity 3 again. Write the answers for you.

1 _____

_____

2 _____

_____

3 _____

_____

4 _____

_____

11

6 | *Is she married?*

GRAMMAR

1 Complete.

is you I Italian he am married are fine she well American it

Verb	Pronoun	Adjective
is	*you*	*Italian*
____	____	____
____	____	____
____	____	____
____	____	____

2 Answer.

Is Steve Italian?   No, *he isn't.* _____

1 Are you British?   No, _____

2 Is Helena from Brazil?   Yes, _____

3 Is Spain a country?   Yes, _____

4 Is the White House in
   Hollywood?   No, _____

5 Is Sarah seventeen?   No, _____

6 Is Marie French?   Yes, _____

3 Correct the sentences.

Damon Hill is an actor. (racing driver)
No, he isn't. He's a racing driver.

1 Tom Cruise is British. (American)
   _____

2 Japanese is a country. (nationality)
   _____

3 Helmut Kohl is Greek. (German)
   _____

4 You are a teacher. (student)
   _____

5 Boston is in Canada. (the United States)
   _____

4 Write questions.

   Is she British? _____
   No, she isn't. She's Canadian.

1 _____
   No, I'm not. I'm Chinese.

2 _____
   Yes, he is. He's from Venice.

3 _____
   No, I'm not married.

4 _____
   Yes, she is.

5 _____
   No, I'm not. I'm a student.

5 Look at the words in *Grammar* activity 1. Write questions.

   Are you married? _____
   _____
   _____
   _____
   _____
   _____
   _____
   _____
   _____

VOCABULARY AND SOUNDS

1 🔊 Listen and write.

   13   ____
   ____   ____
   ____   ____
   ____   ____

2 Write the numbers in activity 1.

thirteen _____ _____

_____ _____

_____ _____

_____ _____

3 Say the numbers in activity 1.

4 Spell.

2 8 11 12 13 20

5 🔊 Listen and check.

READING AND LISTENING

1 Read the descriptions 1 to 4. Write the jobs.

1 *teacher* _____
2 _____
3 _____
4 _____

1 Mayumi is from <u>Bangkok</u>. *Tokyo.* She's Thai. She's a teacher. She isn't married.

2 Eric is a student in Marseilles. He isn't French. He's American. He's from Cambridge in England. He's married.

3 Jorge is a taxi driver. He is married. He's from Madrid in Spain.

4 Amina is Indian. She's from Bombay. She's a secretary in London. She is married.

2 🔊 Listen and underline anything in descriptions 1 to 4 which is different.

3 🔊 Listen again and correct.

WRITING

1 Write about Sean.

INTERNATIONAL
School of English

NAME: *Sean Williams*

AGE: *25*

NATIONALITY: *British*

ADDRESS: *13, North Road, Brighton*

PHONE NUMBER: *01237 691 423*

JOB: *Language teacher*

_____
_____
_____
_____
_____
_____

2 Write about yourself.

name nationality country job
married/not married age

My name's _____
_____
_____
_____
_____
_____
_____
_____

13

7 | *How old is he?*

VOCABULARY AND SOUNDS

1 Match words with the same vowel sounds.

you	from
your	number
job	no
country	two
phone	four

🔲 Listen and check.

2 🔲 Listen again and repeat.

3 🔲 Listen.

/w/: where   what   one   well   work   how
waiter

4 Say the words aloud.

5 Write and say.

35	*thirty-five*	1	_____
18	_____	62	_____
33	_____	99	_____
82	_____	100	_____
45	_____	57	_____

6 🔲 Listen and repeat.

GRAMMAR

1 Complete.

I'm	I'm not	I am not
you're		
he's	_____	_____
she's	_____	_____
it's	_____	_____
	_____	_____

2 Punctuate and write the sentences.

1   what'syourjob

   _____

2   heisn'tfrench

   _____

3   isyournamemaria

   _____

4   howoldisshe

   _____

5   i'mawaiter

   _____

6   you'refrombrazil

   _____

3 Tick (✓) the correct sentence.

1   a   How old he is?
   b   How old is he?
2   a   Are you an engineer?
   b   Are you engineer?
3   a   She's from America.
   b   She's from American.
4   a   I'm from the Rome.
   b   I'm from Rome.
5   a   My favourite car is a Volvo.
   b   My favourite car are a Volvo.

4 Write the questions.

   How old are you?
   _____

   I'm forty.

1   _____

   I'm twenty-four.

2   _____

   He's thirty-one.

3   _____

   She's nineteen.

4   _____

   It's a hundred.

5 Look at the pictures and write questions with *How old?*

A

How old is it?
It's three months.

B

_____
_____
_____
_____

C

_____
_____
_____
_____

D

_____
_____

E

_____
_____
_____
_____

6 Match the ages and answer the questions.

84   9   23   three months   17

LISTENING AND WRITING

1 Look at the pictures of famous people. Write five questions.

   What's your name?
1   How old   _____
2   What's   _____
3   Where are   _____
4   What's   _____
5   Are you   _____

Brad Pitt   Steffi Graf

2 🔊 Listen and match the descriptions with the pictures.

3 🔊 Listen again and complete.

Name:	*Brad Pitt*	*Steffi Graf*
Age:	_____	_____
Nationality:	_____	_____
Town:	_____	_____
Job:	_____	_____
Married:	_____	_____

4 Write descriptions of Brad Pitt and Steffi Graf.

_____
_____
_____
_____
_____
_____
_____
_____
_____
_____
_____

VOCABULARY

1 Complete with words from Lesson 8.

		A	R				
		C			R		
P	L	T					N
		R		U	P		
		E		M			
P	R	S					
		S		G		R	

2 Match.

1	Name	a	taxi driver
2	Nationality	b	thirty-two
3	Job	c	Jean Dupont
4	Age	d	France
5	Country	e	French

3 Write sentences.

1 His name's _____
2 He's _____
3 He's a _____
4 He's _____
5 He's from _____

4 Underline the odd-word-out.

   what   how   <u>from</u>   where   who
1 his   her   he   my   your
2 twenty   nineteen   three   town   eighty
3 Italian   Brazil   French   Japanese   Turkish
4 job   name   married   country   nationality
5 his   he   she   you
6 politician   actor   favourite   presenter

5 Write sentences with the odd-words-out in activity 4.

   Petra is from Rio.
1 _____
2 _____
3 _____
4 _____
5 _____
6 _____

GRAMMAR AND READING

1 Complete.

Subject pronouns	Possessive adjectives
I	my
you	_____
he	_____
she	_____

2 Complete with *his* or *her*.

1 Sarah is a doctor. She's twenty-eight and she's married. _____ favourite singer is Elton John and _____ favourite actor is Tom Cruise. _____ car is a Renault but it isn't _____ favourite car.

2 Mark is from Chicago. He's nineteen and he's a student. _____ favourite group is Oasis. _____ favourite tennis player is Pete Sampras.

3 Put in order and write the sentences.

1 job is his what?

_____

2 Steve name his is

_____

3 is she secretary a?

_____

4 Brazil is Newton from

_____

5 Rio in is Argentina?

_____

6 favourite is his town Marseilles

_____

4 Write *a*, *an* or -.

I'm __*a*__ teacher.

1 I'm _____ actress.

2 Is he _____ Turkish?

3 She's _____ engineer.

4 He's _____ Japanese.

5 Is he _____ teacher?

6 I'm _____ taxi driver.

5 Complete the questions.

where   what   how   who

1 _____ is her name?   a It's in Korea.
2 _____ are you from?   b I'm fine.
3 _____ is his nationality?   c Brad Pitt.
4 _____ is Seoul?   d I'm from
5 _____ is your favourite   Sweden.
  actor?   e She's a
6 _____ are you?   doctor.
7 _____ is her job?   f He's Italian.
                                   g Her name's
                                     Jane.

6 Match the questions and answers.

SOUNDS

🔊 Listen and look.

1 She's American.   5 She's an engineer.
2 Rio isn't in Mexico.   6 Where's Oxford?
3 I'm from Argentina.   7 It's in France.
4 It's in Brazil.

🔊 Listen again and repeat.

LISTENING AND WRITING

1 🔊 Listen and number.

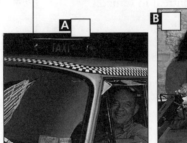  

2 🔊 Listen again and complete.

	Sam	Maria	John
City	_____	_____	_____
Nationality	_____	_____	_____
Job	_____	_____	_____
Favourite singer	_____	_____	_____

3 Look at the example and write about Maria and John.

Sam _*Sam is from New York. He's American. He's a taxi driver. His favourite singer is Phil Collins.*_

Maria _____

_____

_____

_____

John _____

_____

_____

9 | *We're twins*

GRAMMAR AND READING

1 Write the verb *to be*.

I	*am*	it	_____
you	_____	we	_____
he	_____	you	_____
she	_____	they	_____

2 Complete the sentences with the verb *to be*.

We __*are*__ from Montreal in Canada.

1 His name _____ Dan.
2 They _____ doctors.
3 I _____ thirty-five.
4 We _____ not English, we _____
   Australian.
5 _____ he married?
6 Where _____ she from?
7 Ankara _____ in Turkey.
8 How old _____ they?

3 Rewrite the sentences with a subject pronoun.

Brian is Canadian.
He is Canadian.

1 Lee and Joe are twins.

   _____

2 John and I are friends.

   _____

3 Is Sarah from Dublin?

   _____

4 Steve and Sue are my neighbours.

   _____

5 Joseph and I are teachers.

   _____

4 Read and complete.

1 Sarah and I _____ friends. We _____
   Canadian and we _____ from Toronto.
   We _____ students at the university. Sarah
   _____ 21 and I _____ 22.

2 My brothers, Lee and Joe, _____ twins.
   They _____ 25. Lee _____ a doctor
   in London and Joe _____ an engineer in
   Oxford. They _____ not married.

3 Steve and Sue _____ my neighbours. They
   _____ also my friends. Steve _____ a
   teacher and Sue _____ a secretary. They
   _____ married.

5 Answer the questions.

1 What nationality is Sarah?

   _____

2 How old is she?

   _____

3 What town is she from?

   _____

4 Who are twins?

   _____

5 Are the twins married?

   _____

6 Who is a doctor?

   _____

7 Who is a teacher?

   _____

6 Write questions.

   Is he your friend?
   Yes, he is.

1 _____
   No, they aren't.

2 _____
   Yes, we are.

3 _____
   No, she isn't.

4 _____
   Yes, I am.

5 _____
   Yes, they are.

7 Answer the questions for you.

1 Who are your neighbours?

_____

2 Are they your friends, too?

_____

3 Who is your favourite singer?

_____

4 How old are your brothers and sisters?

_____

8 Write the plural.

favourite car _____
English teacher _____
neighbour _____
favourite singer _____
football team _____
French doctor _____

VOCABULARY AND LISTENING

1 Put the letters in order and write words from Lesson 9.

rlig   _girl_   ybo   _____
htobrre   _____   igehnurob   _____
nma   _____   nwaom   _____
rednif   _____   tressi   _____

2 Write the plural of the words in activity 1.

girls   _____
_____   _____
_____   _____
_____   _____

3 Write the words in activity 1 in three groups.

man	woman	man or woman
___	___	___
___	___	___
___	___	___

A

B

4 📼 Listen and match the conversations with the pictures.

5 📼 Listen again and write how old they are.

Conversation 1

Amy: _19_   _nineteen_
Sally: ___   _____
Sam: ___   _____
Teddy: ___   _____
Janet: ___   _____

Conversation 2

John: ___   _____
Tom: ___   _____
Dick: ___   _____
Julia: ___   _____
Emma: ___   _____

WRITING

Write about your brothers and sisters or a friend.

_____
_____
_____
_____
_____
_____
_____

VOCABULARY AND GRAMMAR

1 **Continue the series of words.**

listen sandwich Thai boy ninety Poland
engineer video

1 burger spaghetti pizza ___sandwich___
2 secretary doctor teacher _____
3 read write say _____
4 Canada Spain Australia _____
5 two twelve fourteen _____
6 television clock telephone _____
7 man girl woman _____
8 German Japanese British _____

2 **Write the plurals.**

a wallet ___wallets___
an umbrella _____
a cassette _____
a clock _____
a sandwich _____
a watch _____
a pen _____
a number _____
a bus _____
a key _____

3 **Write the questions.**

___What's this?___
It's a book.

1 _____
They're wallets.

2 _____
It's a taxi.

3 _____
They're keys.

4 _____
It's a sandwich.

4 **Complete the questions with *this*, *that*, *these* or *those*.**

1

2

What's _____ ?   What are _____ ?
It's _____   They're _____

3

4

_____ ?   _____ ?
_____   _____

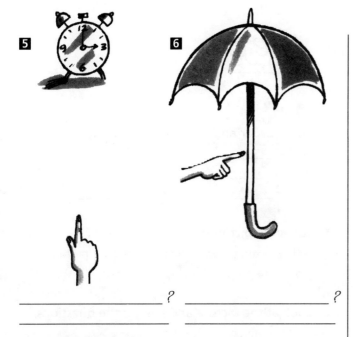

5

6

_____ ?   _____ ?
_____   _____

7

8

_____ ?   _____ ?
_____   _____

5 Write the answers.

6 Ask and answer the questions in activity 5.

7 Complete the questions with *who* or *what* and the verb *to be*.

What are these?   They're my keys.
1 _____ he?   He's my brother.
2 _____ they?   They're friends.
3 _____ that?   It's my umbrella.
4 _____ those? They're my books.
5 _____ she?   She's my neighbour.
6 _____ this?   It's my wallet.

SOUNDS

1 🔊 Listen and repeat the plurals of the words in *Vocabulary and grammar* activity 2.

2 🔊 Listen and tick (✓) the sentences you hear.
1 a What are these?   b What's this?
2 a What's that?   b Who's that?
3 a What are these?   b What's this?
4 a Who are they?   b Who's this?

3 🔊 Listen again and repeat.

READING AND LISTENING

1 Complete with the sentences a – d.

Conversation 1
A (1) _____
B They're cassettes.
A Are they your cassettes?
B No, they aren't.

Conversation 2
A (2) _____
B Yes, they are.
A Is this your dictionary?
B No, it isn't.

Conversation 3
A (3) _____
B It's my car key.
A And what's that?
B I don't know. It isn't my key.

Conversation 4
A (4) _____
B They're Anne and George. They're my neighbours.
A Are they married?
B No! They're brother and sister!

a What's this?   c Are those your books?
b Who are they?   d What are these?

2 🔊 Listen and check.

11 | *How much are they?*

VOCABULARY AND GRAMMAR

1 Write the prices.

1 £13.99 *thirteen pounds ninety-nine pence.*

2 £27.61 _____

3 £84 _____

4 £11.45 _____

5 £129 _____

6 £33.99 _____

7 £2.35 _____

8 89p _____

2 Put in order and write the colours.

eubl _____ neger _____

thiwe _____ dre _____

kalbc _____ lowlye _____

3 Label the picture.

wallets   sunglasses   sweaters   pens   perfume
personal stereos   watches

4 Look at the picture and answer the questions.

How much are the sunglasses?
They're eleven pounds.

1 How much are the watches?

_____

2 How much is the perfume?

_____

3 How much are the wallets?

_____

1 _____   2 _____   3 _____   4 _____

5 _____   6 _____   7 _____

5 Write three questions with *How much?*

1 _____
2 _____
3 _____

6 Answer the questions in activity 5.

1 _____
2 _____
3 _____

7 Look at your clothes. Make a list.

jeans, _____
_____
_____
_____
_____
_____
_____

8 Write the colour of your clothes.

My jeans are blue. _____
_____
_____
_____
_____
_____
_____

LISTENING

1 🔲 Listen and correct.

CUSTOMER How much are these videos?

ASSISTANT They're £13.50.

CUSTOMER And how much are the cassettes?

ASSISTANT They're £8.99.

🔲 Listen again and check.

2 Complete.

CUSTOMER _____ the pizza, please?

ASSISTANT _____ £2.45.

CUSTOMER And _____ the sandwiches?

ASSISTANT _____ 89 pence.

🔲 Listen and check.

3 🔲 Listen and complete.

CUSTOMER How much is this _____ , please?

ASSISTANT It's _____ .

CUSTOMER And how much is that _____ ?

ASSISTANT It's _____ .

🔲 Listen again and check.

GRAMMAR

Write questions.

jacket sunglasses pen jeans shoes shirt

How much is this shirt?
It's fifteen pounds.

1 _____
They're forty-two pounds.

2 _____
It's ninety-nine pence.

3 _____
They're thirty-nine pounds.

4 _____
It's eighty-six pounds.

5 _____
They're seventeen pounds forty-five pence.

VOCABULARY

Write the name of the objects.

GRAMMAR

1 Match.

in   on   under

1 _____   2 _____   3 _____

2 Look at the picture in *Vocabulary*. Complete the sentences.

The wallet is _*in*_ the bag.

1 The sunglasses are _____ the chair.

2 The bag is _____ the table.

3 The postcard is _____ the bag.

4 The radio is _____ the table.

24 5 The photos are _____ the table.

3 Where are they? Write sentences.

1 The books _____

2 The keys _____

3 The watch _____

4 The coat _____

5 The pen _____

4 Match the questions and the pictures.

1 Who's this. ☐   3 What are these? ☐

2 What's this? ☐   4 Who are they? ☐

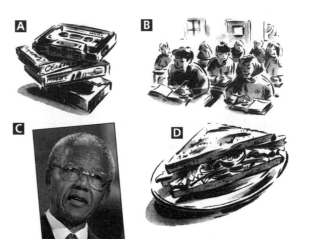

5 Answer the questions.

1 _____

2 _____

3 _____

4 _____

6 Underline the *'s* possessive and circle the *'s* verb *is*.

It(s)Harry's bag.

1 Where's my wallet?

2 My brother's name's Sam.

3 What's this book on the table?

4 Annie's photos are on the table.

5 Who's this?

6 It's Sally's dictionary.

7 Look at the pictures. Write sentences with the possessive *'s*. Write sentences with *his* or *her*.

Example:

1 This is Reza's watch.

 This is his watch.

1 _____

 _____

2 _____

 _____

3 _____

 _____

4 _____

 _____

5 _____

 _____

6 _____

 _____

This is Nathalie. This is Reza.

LISTENING

1 Read questions from three conversations.

	Conversation 1	Conversation 2	Conversation 3
1 What's in your bag?	☐	✔	☐
2 What's his name?	☐	☐	☐
3 What are they?	☐	☐	☐
4 Where is she?	☐	☐	☐
5 Is he a student?	☐	☐	☐
6 Is this it?	☐	☐	☐

2 🔊 Listen to the conversations. Match the questions and conversations.

3 🔊 Listen again and match the questions in activity 1 with these answers.

a ☐ Oasis and U2.

b ☐ Yes, he is.

c ☐ At work.

d ☐ A book, my wallet, my keys and two pens.

e ☐ Yes, it is.

f ☐ Amado. Enrico Amado.

25

We've got three children

VOCABULARY

1 Put the letters in order and write *family* words.

hertaf _father_   nso _____

htgdeuar _____   dsabhnu _____

retsis _____   rrbeoth _____

feiw _____   eromth _____

2 Put the words in 1 into two groups.

man	woman
_____	_____
_____	_____
_____	_____
_____	_____

GRAMMAR AND READING

1 Complete.

Pronouns	Possessive adjectives
_I_	_my_
you	_____
_____	_____
_____	_____
_____	_____
_____	_____
_____	_____

2 Underline the correct form.

They/their are from Japan.

1 Tony is our/are son.

2 Sally is their/they're mother.

3 Where are you/your from?

4 Are they/their doctors?

5 John and Sue are/our married.

3 Answer the questions for you.

Have you got a television?
Yes, I have.

1 Have you got any brothers and sisters?

_____

2 Have you got any children?

_____

3 Have you got a car?

_____

4 Have you got a video?

_____

5 Have you got a personal stereo?

_____

6 Have you got any jeans?

_____

4 Write questions.

1 _____

_____

Yes, I have.

2 _____

_____

No, I haven't.

3 _____

_____

Yes, I have.

4 _____

_____

No, I haven't.

5 Read and complete with pronouns and possessive adjectives.

Hello, (1) _____ name's Sally and this is (2) _____ family. (3) _____ are from Birmingham in England. (4) _____ husband is Paul. (5) _____ is fifty-nine and (6) _____ is a bus driver. (7) _____ have got three children, two daughters and a son. (8) _____ daughter Jennifer is married and (9) _____ husband Tom is a policeman. (10) _____ daughter Sue is nineteen. (11) _____ isn't married and

(12) _____ is a student in Brussels. Charlie,
(13) _____ son, is twenty-seven. (14) _____
is married. (15) _____ is a teacher at the
university and (16) _____ wife, Shirley, is a
doctor. They have got a son, Jim.

6 **Read and write the names of the family in the picture. Then answer the questions.**

Is Paul married?
Yes, he is. His wife is Sally.

1 Where are Sally and Paul from?

_____

2 Who is Sue?

_____

3 How old is Sue?

_____

4 Who is Charlie?

_____

5 How old is Charlie?

_____

6 What is Shirley's job?

_____

7 Have Charlie and Shirley got any children?

_____

8 What is their son's name?

_____

LISTENING

Listen and match the questions and the conversations.

Conversation 1: ☐

Conversation 2: ☐

Conversation 3: ☐

a Have you got any children?
b Have you got any brothers and sisters?
c Have you got a car?

WRITING

Complete for your parents.
My mother is 52. She's a teacher. She's German and she's from Bonn.

My mother is _____ . She's a
_____ . She's _____ and
she's from _____ .

My father is _____ . He's a
_____ . He's _____ and he's
from _____ .

1 _____ + 2 _____

3 _____ + 4 _____   5 _____ + 6 _____   7 _____

8 _____

27

14 | *She's got fair hair and blue eyes*

VOCABULARY

1 Find 14 adjectives from Lesson 14.

S	P	Q	U	I	E	T	F
H	R	C	L	E	V	E	R
O	E	D	F	A	I	R	I
R	T	A	W	H	I	T	E
T	T		R	E	D	B	N
F	Y	K	T	A	L	L	D
U	B	L	A	C	K	U	L
N	G	R	E	E	N	E	Y

quiet, _____

_____

_____

_____

2 Complete for you.

1 I've got _____ eyes.
2 My mother has got _____ hair.
3 My friend is quite _____ .
4 My father has got _____ hair and _____ eyes.
5 My friend is very _____ and quite _____ .

GRAMMAR

1 Complete the verb *to have got*.

I	*'ve got*	*have got*	*haven't got*
you	_____	_____	_____
he	_____	_____	_____
she	_____	_____	_____
we	_____	_____	_____
they	_____	_____	_____

2 Complete.

1 I _____ fair hair and blue eyes.
2 He _____ two brothers.
3 She _____ a black car.
4 We _____ any children.
5 He _____ any brothers and sisters.
6 They _____ a son and a daughter.

3 Put in order and write the sentences.

1 like she what's ?

_____

2 brown got she's eyes

_____

3 haven't and I sisters got brothers any

_____

4 Bill is name brother's my

_____

5 hair got he's fair

_____

6 got children any haven't they

_____

4 Tick (✓) the correct sentence.

1 a He's got very friendly.　b He's very friendly.
2 a She's got brown eyes.　b She's brown eyes.
3 a I've got twenty-two.　b I'm twenty-two.
4 a She's very quiet.　b She's got very quiet.
5 a My brother's got　b My brother's quite
　　quite tall.　　tall.
6 a My father hasn't got　b My father isn't any
　　any hair.　　hair.

5 Match the questions and answers.

1 How old is he?　　　　　a They're brown.
2 What's she like?　　　　b No, she hasn't.
3 Is he tall?　　　　　　　c She's very nice.
4 What colour are her eyes?　d He's eighteen.
5 Has she got any children?　e No, he's quite short.

6 Complete for you.

1   My brother's got _____

_____

2   My parents have got _____

_____

3   I haven't got _____

_____

4   My neighbours have got _____

_____

5   My sister's got _____

_____

SOUNDS

🔊 Listen and repeat.

1   I've got a brother.
2   She's got a video.
3   We've got a neighbour.
4   He hasn't got any hair.
5   They haven't got a car.

READING

1   Read and write the names.

My name's Christine Trent. I'm twenty-two and I'm not very tall. I've got dark hair and brown eyes. I've got a brother and twin sisters. My brother's name is Graham. He's an engineer. He's twenty-five and he's very good-looking. He's tall and he's got black hair and blue eyes. My twin sisters, Amy and Liza, are fifteen. They are very quiet. They've got fair hair and blue eyes. They are very clever. My mother's name is Joan. She's very nice and friendly. She's quite short and she's got fair hair. My father's name is Fred. He's very tall and he hasn't got any hair. He's fun.

2   Correct the statements.

Christine is very tall and dark.
She isn't very tall. _____

1   Graham is Christine's father.

_____

2   Graham has got fair hair.

_____

3   Her sisters are fifteen and thirteen.

_____

4   Her mother's name is Amy.

_____

5   Fred has got dark hair.

_____

2 _____   3 _____

1 _____

4 _____   5 _____

15 | *Stand up!*

VOCABULARY AND GRAMMAR

1 Match.

Box A	Box B
stand sit turn pick come take put	up on in off down

stand up, _____

_____

_____

2 Complete.

light jacket books bag CD window letter cassette player coat

Open your *books.*

1 Don't close the _____

2 Put your _____ on.

3 Turn the _____ off.

4 Pick your _____ up.

5 Read this _____

6 Take your _____ off.

7 Put the _____ on the table.

8 Listen to this _____

3 Write instructions with these words.

homework door television window light coat book

Do your homework.

_____

_____

_____

_____

_____

4 Write the negative.

Look!

Don't look!

1 Do activity 2.

_____

_____

2 Open the window.

_____

3 Turn the cassette player off.

_____

4 Read the instructions.

_____

5 Close your books.

_____

_____

6 Read the letter.

_____

_____

5 Write instructions for your English class. Use these words.

smoke speak listen worry look close open read

Don't smoke in the classroom.

_____

_____

_____

_____

_____

_____

_____

_____

_____

READING AND LISTENING

1 Read A, B and C and match them with these situations.

in a restaurant   in the classroom   in a car
at home   in a plane

A

Ladies and gentlemen the plane is ready for take off.
Put your bags in the hand luggage compartment.
Please (1) _____ and fasten your seat belts.
(2) _____ and don't use mobile telephones or computers.

B

A Sit down. John, (3) _____ the door, please. Thank you.
B What lesson is it today, Mr James?
A Lesson 16. (4) _____ your books at page 43. Do activities 3 and 5.
B What about number 4?
A No, (5) _____ that. Greg Smith! (6) _____ to your personal stereo in class!
(7) _____ it in your bag!

C

CLAIRE Hello, Jane. How are you?
JANE Hello, Claire. I'm fine. And you, how is the family?
CLAIRE We're all very well. But don't stand outside. (8) _____ and have a cup of tea.
JANE Thanks.
CLAIRE (9) _____ your coat _____ .
(10) _____ . Would you like coffee or tea?
JANE Tea, please.
CLAIRE Have some cake. It's chocolate and orange.
JANE Thank you very much.

2 Complete A, B and C with these instructions.

don't smoke   don't listen   sit down   take off
don't do   sit down   put   open   come in   close

🔲 Listen and check.

SOUNDS

1 🔲 Listen and look.
Stand up.
Pick it up.
Turn it off.
Come in.
Take your coat off.
Put the light on.

Say the instructions.

2 🔲 Listen and look.
Sit down.
Don't close the door.
Don't read that book.
Don't look.

3 🔲 Listen again and repeat.

16 | *We live in a flat in Florence*

VOCABULARY

1 Complete the crossword.

Across:

2 I'm a teacher and I work in a _____ .

4 We are waiters and we _____ in a restaurant.

5 I live in a _____ .

7 Come in and take off your _____ .

9 We _____ in a house in Birmingham.

11 Turn _____ the light, please.

Down:

1 They _____ to school in Istanbul.

2 They work in a clothes _____ .

3 We are secretaries and we work in an _____ in London.

6 Turn _____ the light. It's not dark.

8 I go _____ school in Lyon.

10 They work _____ a shop _____ Cardiff.

2 Continue the series of words.

read our sweater daughter skirt she office mother their we close house

1 I you he __*she*__ _____

2 stand sit go _____ _____

3 shop flat school _____ _____

4 her your his _____ _____

5 son brother sister _____ _____

6 coat shirt jacket _____ _____

3 Complete these sentences for you.

1 I'm a/an _____
   _____ .

2 I live in a _____
   in _____ .

3 I go to _____
   in _____ .

5 My parents live in a _____
   in _____ .

6 I've got _____
   and _____ .

7 I haven't got _____
   _____ .

GRAMMAR AND WRITING

1 Complete with *in* or *to*.

1 They work _____ a shop _____ Paris.

2 We go _____ school _____ Rome.

3 I live _____ a flat _____ Venice.

4 Our neighbours live _____ a house.

5 I work _____ an office _____ New York.

6 They go _____ school in Madrid.

2 Write sentences.

I	live	flat
We	work	school
You	go	office
		shop
		house

I live in a flat.
_____
_____
_____
_____
_____
_____

3 Match the jobs with the places.

doctor	classroom
secretary	restaurant
shop assistant	office
teacher	shop
waiter	hospital

4 Look at picture 1. Write similar sentences for pictures 2 to 5.

2 Turkey

4 Mexico

SOUNDS

1 Listen and look.

1 I <u>live</u> in a <u>flat</u> in <u>Glasgow</u>.
2 <u>Where</u> do you <u>work</u>?
3 I'm <u>married</u>.
4 I <u>work</u> in an <u>office</u>.
5 They're <u>doctors</u>.
6 I <u>work</u> in a <u>hospital</u> in <u>Valencia</u>.

2 Listen again and repeat.

I live in Italy. I'm a doctor and I work in a hospital.

1 Italy

3 Japan

5 France

33

VOCABULARY

1 Match.

seven am   two pm   eight pm   eleven am
six pm   three pm

1 _____

2 _____

3 _____

4 _____

5 _____

6 _____

2 Write the time.

7 am   *It's seven o'clock in the morning.*
8 pm   _____
11 am _____
3 pm   _____
6 pm   _____
2 pm   _____

GRAMMAR

1 Write the present simple of these verbs.

	to have	to work	to live	to be
I	_____	_____	_____	_____
you	_____	_____	_____	_____
we	_____	_____	_____	_____
they	_____	_____	_____	_____

2 Complete with *in* or *at*.

1 In Turkey we have breakfast _____ seven o'clock _____ the morning.
2 I work _____ the afternoon.
3 Washington is _____ the United States.
4 We live _____ a flat _____ Paris.
5 I have lunch _____ twelve o'clock.
6 They have dinner _____ eight o'clock _____ the evening.

3 Match.

	in a flat.
I have	in an office.
We work	breakfast at 8 o'clock.
They live	in a shop.
	lunch in the afternoon.
	in a house in Florence.

4 Write questions for these answers.

1 *Where are you from?*
  I'm from New York.
2 _____
  It's seven o'clock.
3 _____
  I'm a secretary.
4 _____
  I'm French.
5 _____
  Yes, I've got two brothers.
6 _____
  I'm seventeen.

5 Answer the questions in activity 4 for you.

1 _____
2 _____
3 _____
4 _____
5 _____
6 _____

READING

1 **Read passage A and underline the jobs.**

A
Hello. My name's Pierre Dupont. I live in France. I'm a doctor in a hospital in Toulouse. My wife, Claire, is an English teacher in a school. We have breakfast at seven o'clock in the morning. I have lunch at one o'clock at the hospital – a sandwich. My wife and I and our three children have dinner at our house at eight o'clock in the evening.

2 **Read passage B and underline the verbs.**

B
Hello. My name's Christine Simpson. I'm English. I live in a flat in Liverpool. I'm a secretary and I work in an office. My husband, Jan, is Polish. He's a television actor. In the morning, at eight o'clock, I have breakfast with my husband and son, Steve. I have lunch at one o'clock at the office. We have dinner at six o'clock in the evening.

3 **Look at passages A and B and write the times.**

Pierre
breakfast   *Seven o'clock in the morning*
lunch   _____
dinner   _____

Christine
breakfast   _____
lunch   _____
dinner   _____

4 **Read A and correct these statements**

Pierre is from Italy.
No. Pierre is from France.

1 Pierre and Claire live in Paris.
_____

2 Pierre is a secretary in an office.
_____

3 They have breakfast at eight o'clock.
_____

4 They have dinner at six o'clock in the evening.
_____

5 **Read B and answer these questions.**

1 What is Christine's nationality?
_____

2 Is Jan British?
_____

3 What's Christine's job?
_____

4 What's their son's name?
_____

5 What time's dinner in their house?
_____

WRITING

Write about you.
job   live   work   breakfast   lunch   dinner
I'm a _____
_____
_____
_____
_____
_____
_____
_____
_____

18 | *I don't like Monday mornings*

VOCABULARY

1 Write the days of the week.

M_____   F_____
T_____   S_____
W_____   S_____
Th_____

2 Put these words in three groups.

newspaper   tennis   letter   book   music   radio
postcard   football   CD   baseball

play	read	listen to
tennis	_____	_____
_____	_____	_____
_____	_____	_____
_____	_____	_____
_____	_____	_____

GRAMMAR

1 Punctuate the passage.

i work in a shop from monday to friday in the
evening i read or i watch television on friday i go
to the cinema with friends on saturday morning i
go shopping and in the afternoon i watch the sport
on television or i play tennis with my son on
sunday i have breakfast at eleven o'clock with my
family and we go to see my parents in the
afternoon my favourite day is sunday

I work in a shop from Monday to Friday.

_____
_____
_____
_____
_____
_____
_____

2 Tick (✓) the sentences that are true for you.

1 I play football. ☐
2 I go to the cinema in the evening. ☐
3 I live in a flat. ☐
4 I work in an office. ☐
5 I live with my parents. ☐
6 I like tennis. ☐
7 I read the newspaper in the morning. ☐
8 I see my friends on Saturday evening. ☐

3 Write the sentences in the negative.

1 *I don't play football.*
2 _____
3 _____
4 _____
5 _____
6 _____
7 _____
8 _____

SOUNDS

1 Put these words in two groups.

afternoon   today   morning   cinema   Wednesday
breakfast   birthday   radio   Saturday   shopping

two syllables:
today
_____

three syllables:
afternoon
_____

🔊 Listen and check.

2 🔊 Listen and underline the silent letters.

two   daughter   Wednesday   listen   eight
sandwich   answer   light

36

READING AND WRITING

1 Look at the pictures. Write the time and the day under the pictures.

1 *It's eleven o'clock on Saturday morning.*

2 _____

3 _____

4 _____

5 _____

6 _____

2 Look at the pictures and write sentences.
1 *They play tennis on Saturday morning.*
2 _____
3 _____
4 _____
5 _____
6 _____

3 Read and underline the verbs.
My favourite day is Saturday. I don't work on Saturday. I have breakfast at 10 o'clock and I read the newspaper and listen to the radio. I go shopping for food and drink. In the afternoon my brother and I play tennis. In the evening I see my friends and we go to the cinema or to a disco.

4 Complete the sentences for you.
1 I don't like _____
2 My favourite day is _____
3 From Monday to Friday I _____
4 On Monday morning I _____
5 On Wednesday evening I don't _____
6 In the evening I _____
7 On Saturday I don't _____
8 On Sunday morning I _____

5 Read the text in activity 3. Write about your favourite day.
My favourite day is _____
_____
_____
_____
_____
_____
_____
_____

19 | *Do you like running?*

VOCABULARY

1 Label the pictures.

1 _____

2 _____

3 _____

4 _____

5 _____

6 _____

7 _____

8 _____

9 _____

2 Write four sentences with words in activity 1.

1 *I like chocolate very much.*

2 _____

3 _____

4 _____

3 Complete the sentences.

work   live   like   have

Do you ___*live*___ in Madrid?

1 Do they _____ chocolate?

2 Do you _____ dinner at eight o'clock in the evening?

3 I don't _____ tennis very much.

4 I _____ in a house in Brighton.

5 They _____ in a hospital.

6 We _____ coffee in the morning.

7 They _____ breakfast at seven o'clock in the morning.

8 Do you _____ in an office?

LISTENING AND SPEAKING

1 Complete the dialogue.

SYLVIE Do you like beer, Mike?

MIKE (1) _____. I like beer very much.

SYLVIE And do you like tea?

MIKE (2) _____ .

a No, I don't.

b Yes, I do.

2 🔲 Listen and check.

3 🔲 Listen and complete.

1 Do you like _____ ?

2 Do you like _____ ?

3 Do you like _____ ?

4 Do you like _____ ?

5 Do you like _____ ?

4 Answer the questions in activity 3 for you.

1 _____
2 _____
3 _____
4 _____
5 _____

GRAMMAR

1 Put in order and write the sentences.

1 like tennis you do?

_____

2 much like very they sport

_____

3 an do in office you work?

_____

4 live a you flat do in?

_____

5 in London live house I a in

_____

6 you lunch have at do home?

_____

2 Answer the questions in 1 for you.

_____
_____
_____
_____

3 Write questions for these answers.

1 _____

No, I don't.

2 _____

Yes, we are.

3 _____

No, I'm not.

4 _____

Yes, they do.

5 _____

No, they don't.

6 _____

Yes, I have.

7 _____

Yes, very much.

SOUNDS

1 🔊 Listen and look.

1 <u>Do you</u> like coffee?
2 <u>Do you</u> have breakfast at eight o'clock?
3 <u>Do you</u> work in a shop?
4 <u>Do you</u> live in a house?

2 🔊 Listen again and repeat.

3 🔊 Listen.

/tʃ/: chair   chocolate   teacher   watch   much
      lunch   French   children

/ʃ/: shop   fish   short   shoes   shirt   politician
      she   nationality

Say the words aloud.

WRITING

1 Write five things you like doing.

_____
_____
_____
_____
_____
_____

2 Write five things you don't like doing.

_____
_____
_____
_____
_____
_____
_____

20 | *She likes her job*

VOCABULARY AND SOUNDS

1 Write the time.

1 *a quarter past three*

2 _____

3 _____

4 _____

5 _____

6 _____

2 🔊 Listen and repeat.

40

3 Find 16 verbs in the puzzle.

L	S	T	A	R	T	B	F
I	P	L	A	Y	L	E	I
V	R	E	A	D	I	S	N
E	W	W	O	R	K	E	I
H	R	D	G	O	E	E	S
A	I	O	W	A	T	C	H
V	T	A	R	R	I	V	E
E	E	L	E	A	V	E	X

start, _____

_____

_____

4 Complete with verbs from the puzzle in activity 3.

I _*watch*_ television in the evenings.

1 He _____ work at nine o'clock in the morning.

2 We _____ home at a quarter past six in the evening.

3 I _____ letters to my friends on Saturdays.

4 She _____ lunch at noon.

5 They _____ football on Saturday afternoons.

6 We _____ our friends in the evenings.

GRAMMAR

1 Write the verbs.

	to have	**to go**	**to finish**
I	*have*	_____	_____
you	_____	_____	_____
he/she	_____	_____	_____
we	_____	_____	_____
they	_____	_____	_____

2 Answer the questions.

1 Where do you work or go to school?
I work/go to school

2 When do you leave home in the morning?

3 When do you start work?

4 When do you finish work?

5 When do you arrive home?

6 What do you do in the evening?

3 Write sentences with he or she.

1 work/office *He/she works in an office.*

2 leave home/8.15 am

3 start work/9.00 am

4 finish work/4 pm

5 arrive home/4.45 pm

6 watch television/evening

READING

1 Number the sentences.

a Jenny leaves home and goes to work at a quarter past eight.

b She has lunch with a friend at half past twelve.

c Jenny has breakfast with her husband at a quarter to eight.

d She watches television with her family from seven to half past nine in the evening.

e She arrives at her office at a quarter to nine.

f She leaves the office at half past four.

g She starts work again at half past one.

h She has a cup of coffee at work at a quarter to eleven.

2 Correct these sentences.

1 Jenny has breakfast with her children.

2 She arrives at work at nine o'clock.

3 She has lunch with her husband at a quarter to one.

4 In the afternoon she leaves the office at five o'clock.

5 In the evening she sees friends.

LISTENING

1 Listen and write the time.

A What time do you have breakfast, Maggie?

B At _____ . I have breakfast with my family. I leave home at _____ .

A When do you arrive at work?

B At _____ . I have a cup of coffee with a friend and I start work at _____ .

A Do you go home for lunch?

B Yes, I have lunch at _____ with my sister. We have a sandwich and fruit juice.

A When do you finish work in the evening?

B At _____ . I arrive home at _____ and I have a cup of tea.

2 Listen again and check.

3 Complete.

1 Maggie _____ breakfast with her family.
2 She _____ at work at 8.45.
3 She _____ a cup of coffee with a friend.
4 She _____ home for lunch.
5 She _____ work at 5.30.

41

VOCABULARY

1 Do the crossword.

Across:

2

3

Down:

1

2

3

4

2 Tick (✓) for you.

1 I've got a bicycle. ☐

2 I don't walk to work. ☐

3 I don't like boats. ☐

4 I go to work by bus. ☐

5 I go shopping in town by car. ☐

6 I don't go to work by train. ☐

GRAMMAR

1 Complete with *do, don't, does* or *doesn't*.

___Do___ you like tennis? No, I ___don't.___

1 _____ your sister live with you?
No, she _____ .

2 _____ he go to work by car?
Yes, he _____ .

3 _____ they live in Budapest?
No, they _____ .

4 _____ you go to school by bus?
Yes, I _____ .

5 _____ she visit her parents at the
weekend?
No, she _____ .

6 _____ you work in the hospital?
Yes, we _____ .

2 Answer the questions.

Do you live with your parents?
No, I don't.

1 Does your sister/brother live with you?
_____

2 Does your father work now?
_____

3 Do you go to work/school by bus?
_____

4 Does your English teacher work in the evening?
_____

5 Do you leave home at eight o'clock?
_____

6 Do your parents speak English?
_____

7 Does your mother have a job?
_____

8 Do your friends learn English too?
_____

3 Put in order and write the questions.

1 go by he car work to does?

_____

2 walk you school to do?

_____

3 television they watch do football on?

_____

4 taxi does home by she go?

_____

5 he lunch work at does have?

_____

4 Write questions for these answers.

Do you go to work by bus?

No, I don't. I go by car.

1 _____?

Yes, I do.

2 _____?

No, he doesn't. He walks to school.

3 _____?

No, we don't. We go by train.

4 _____?

No, I'm not. I'm a teacher.

5 _____?

Yes, she does.

6 _____?

No, they don't. They live in a flat.

SOUNDS

1 Match the same vowel sound.

train	does
time	read
bus	don't
leave	day
boat	start
car	like

2 🔊 Listen and check.

READING AND LISTENING

1 Read and complete with sentences a–g.

MARY Hello. My name's Mary. I work at a language school. Are you a student?

KEVIN Hello, Mary. No, I'm not a student. I'm a teacher. My name's Kevin.

MARY (1) _____

KEVIN At the International School in London.

MARY (2) _____

KEVIN No, I live with my brother in Bath.

MARY (3) _____

KEVIN I work on Monday, Tuesday, Wednesday and Friday. I start work at half past nine in the morning.

MARY (4) _____

KEVIN I leave home at a quarter past seven. I go to London by train.

MARY (5) _____

KEVIN It leaves at a quarter to eight and it arrives in London at a quarter to nine.

MARY (6) _____

KEVIN I finish work at a quarter to four. And I arrive home at half past six.

MARY (7) _____

KEVIN I have breakfast in bed at eleven o'clock!

a When do you leave home in the morning?
b What do you do on Thursday?
c Do you live in London?
d Where do you work?
e And when do you finish work and go home?
f When do you work?
g When does your train leave?

2 🔊 Listen and check.

3 Complete.

Kevin is a teacher. He _____ at the International School. He _____ in Bath not in London. He _____ on Monday, Tuesday, Wednesday and Friday. He _____ work at 9.30 in the morning. He _____ home at 7.15 in the morning. He _____ work at 3.45 in the afternoon and he _____ home at 6.30. On Thursday he _____ breakfast in bed at 11.00.

VOCABULARY AND LISTENING

1 **Label the food and drink.**

2 🔊 **Listen and tick (✓) the question John answers.**

1 What do you drink with your lunch? ☐

2 What's your favourite meal? ☐

3 When do you have breakfast? ☐

3 🔊 **Listen again and complete.**

1 He doesn't eat much for _____ .

2 His favourite meal is _____ .

3 John has _____ at 7.30.

4 He drinks _____ for breakfast.

5 He eats an _____ and toast with _____ .

4 🔊 **Listen and tick (✓) what Helen says.**

1 My favourite meal is lunch. ☐

2 I have a big breakfast. ☐

3 I have lunch at home. ☐

4 I don't like rice. ☐

5 I like meat. ☐

6 I don't like vegetables. ☐

7 I drink fruit juice with my lunch. ☐

8 I don't drink wine. ☐

GRAMMAR

1 **Write the verbs in the negative.**

	to eat	**to drink**
I	*don't eat*	_____
you	_____	_____
he/she/it	_____	_____
we	_____	_____
they	_____	_____

2 **Write the sentences in the negative.**

He likes work.
He doesn't like work.

1 I start work at half past nine.

_____

2 She eats dinner at home.

_____

3 They like beer.

_____

4 He works in an office.

_____

5 She lives in a flat.

_____

3 **Write the questions.**

Where do you live?
I live in Turkey.

1 What _____

I have coffee and bread.

2 When _____

I drink beer with my lunch.

3 Where _____

I work in a shop.

4 What _____

I watch television.

5 When _____

I start work at nine o'clock.

6 What _____

I like apples.

4 Answer the questions for you.

1 _____
2 _____
3 _____
4 _____
5 _____
6 _____

READING AND WRITING

1 Read and match the passage with the picture.
My favourite meal is dinner. I watch television and have dinner at eight o'clock. I don't eat much for lunch – just a sandwich and an apple – so I have a big dinner. I have a salad then I eat meat or fish with vegetables. I like Mexican food very much. I have chili con carne or tortilla on Friday evening. I don't like beer, I usually drink red wine. I don't eat fruit or drink coffee in the evening.

2 Write the text in the third person.
His favourite meal is dinner.
_____
_____
_____
_____
_____
_____
_____
_____

3 Write a text for picture B. Here are some words you can use.

barbecue friends garden salad summer sun
Her favourite meal is _____
_____
_____
_____
_____
_____
_____
_____

4 Write about your favourite meal.
_____
_____
_____
_____
_____
_____
_____

23 | *I don't like lying on the beach*

VOCABULARY

1 Match.

Box A	Box B
read stay lie	at home in the sea at a hotel
swim ski	the newspaper on the beach
cook eat	in restaurants a book in a flat
	dinner in the mountains

read the newspaper, _____

_____

_____

_____

_____

_____

2 Complete.

skiing   staying   lying   go   stay   swimming
read   watch   cooking   eat

1 I _____ to the sea for my summer holiday.
   I like _____ on the beach and the children
   like _____ in the sea.

2 I go _____ in the Alps with friends. We
   _____ in a holiday flat for a week. We
   don't like _____ so we _____ in
   restaurants.

3 I don't _____ on holiday. I like
   _____ at home. I _____ the
   newspaper and I _____ television.

SOUNDS

🔊 **Listen and repeat.**

1 When do you go on <u>holiday</u>?
2 Who do you <u>go</u> with?
3 What do you do in <u>July</u>?
4 Where do you go for your <u>holiday</u>?
5 How do you get to <u>work</u>?

LISTENING

1 Put a tick (✓) by the things you *like doing*. Put a cross (✗) by the things you *don't like doing*.

	You	Mike	Karen
food shopping			
shopping for clothes			
walking			
watching television			
lying on the beach			
sightseeing			
working			
listening to rock music			
skiing			
writing postcards			
dancing			

2 🔊 Listen and put a tick (✓) by the things Mike and Karen *like doing*. Put a cross (✗) by the things they *don't like doing*.

3 🔊 Listen again and check.

GRAMMAR

1 Complete for Mike.

1 Mike _____ shopping for clothes but
   he _____ doing the food shopping.
   He's a student and he _____
   working. When he goes on holiday he
   _____ on the beach and
   _____ to rock music on his personal
   stereo. He _____ writing postcards.
   He _____ sightseeing and he
   _____ walking when he's on
   holiday. He _____ in the evenings in
   nightclubs.

46

2 Write three things Karen *likes doing*.
She likes reading.
_____
_____
_____

3 Write two things she *doesn't like doing*.
She doesn't like watching television.
_____
_____

4 Complete with a question word.

what   who   where   when   how

1 _____ do you go with on holiday?
2 _____ do you do on Saturday?
3 _____ do you go on holiday?
4 _____ do you get to work?
5 _____ do you live?
6 _____ do you like doing in the evenings?
7 _____ do you finish work?
8 _____ do you live with?

5 Answer the questions in activity 4 for you.

1 _____
   _____
2 _____
   _____
3 _____
   _____
4 _____
   _____
5 _____
   _____
6 _____
   _____
7 _____
   _____
8 _____
   _____

6 Write questions.

1 *Do you like lying on the beach?*
   Yes, I do.
2 _____
   No, they don't.
3 _____
   She likes sightseeing.
4 _____
   In July.
5 _____
   To the cinema.
6 _____
   I go by train.

7 Complete with *in, at* or *on*.

1 He watches television _____ the evenings.
2 We go to see my parents _____ Sunday.
3 She goes _____ holiday _____ August.
4 We have lunch _____ a quarter past twelve.
5 _____ the morning, I leave for work _____ eight o'clock.
6 _____ February I like to go skiing.
7 I don't work _____ Monday.
8 We go walking _____ Saturday afternoons.

WRITING

Write about what you like doing on holiday.

_____
_____
_____
_____
_____
_____
_____
_____
_____
_____
_____

24 | *There's a telephone in the hall*

VOCABULARY

1 Put in order and write the names of parts of the home.

chntike _____   mdoreob _____

graage _____   yobnlac _____

ndrgae _____   otbaohmr _____

tlteoi _____   vginli moro _____

2 Complete for your house.

There's ___*a fridge*___ in the kitchen.

There's _____ in the bathroom.

There are _____ in the living room.

There are _____ in the kitchen.

There's a _____ in the bedroom.

There's a _____ in the garage.

There's a _____ in the kitchen.

GRAMMAR

1 Complete with *is* or *are*.

1 There _____ plants in the hall.

2 There _____ a shower in the bathroom.

3 There _____ a television on the table.

4 There _____ two armchairs in the living room.

5 There _____ cupboards in the kitchen.

6 There _____ a telephone in the bedroom.

2 Write the sentences in activity 1 in the negative.

1 *There aren't any plants in the hall.*

2 _____

3 _____

4 _____

5 _____

6 _____

3 Answer for your house.

Is there a sofa in the living room of your house?
Yes, there is.

1 Is there a table in your bedroom?

_____

2 Are there any armchairs in the living room?

_____

3 Is there a window in the bathroom?

_____

4 Are there any cupboards in the kitchen?

_____

5 Is there a television in your bedroom?

_____

READING AND WRITING

1 Write about the homes in the pictures.

A

It's a flat. There's a _____

It's a _____

B

_____

_____

2 Read and match the advertisements for holiday homes with the pictures.

1
> Come skiing in the French Alps!
> House for six to eight people.
> Kitchen with washing machine.
> Two bedrooms, a bathroom with shower.
> A living room with a sofa-bed.

2
> A holiday flat by the sea on the Spanish Riviera.
> For four people. One bedroom, a kitchen.
> A sofa-bed in the living room.
> A bathroom with shower.
> A balcony with table and chairs.

3
> A family holiday in Scotland.
> House for eight to ten people.
> Four bedrooms, two bathrooms.
> Kitchen with washing machine and fridge.
> Living room with TV and video.
> Garden and garage for two cars

C

_____

_____

3 Read the advertisements and write sentences with *there is/are*.

1 There's a washing machine in the
  kitchen.

_____

_____

_____

_____

_____

2 There's one bedroom.

_____

_____

_____

_____

_____

3 There are four bedrooms.

_____

_____

_____

_____

_____

LISTENING

1 🔲 Listen and match the conversation with the correct advertisement.

2 🔲 Listen again and complete.

1 The flat is on the _____ Riviera.

2 It's for a family of _____ .

3 There are _____ _____ in the bedroom.

4 There's a _____ _____ in the living room.

5 There's a _____ _____ in the kitchen.

6 There isn't a _____ .

7 There's a _____ on the balcony.

8 It's £_____ for a week in July.

25 *I usually have a party*

VOCABULARY AND SOUNDS

1 Write the months of the year.

J*anuary*   J_____

F_____   A_____

M_____   S_____

A_____   O_____

M_____   N_____

J_____   D_____

2 🔊 Listen and underline the stressed syllables. Say the months.

3 Write.

1st *first*   6th _____

2nd _____   7th _____

3rd _____   8th _____

4th _____   9th _____

5th _____   10th _____

4 🔊 Listen and repeat.

5 Write the dates.

1/7 *the first of July*_____

23/9 _____

16/5 _____

2/4 _____

15/2 _____

30/10 _____

1/8_____

6 🔊 Listen and check.

7 Say the dates.

8 Complete for you and your country.

1   In my country we never work on

     _____ .

2   _____ is a national holiday.

3   The _____ birthday is always very special.

4   After the summer holiday, children return to school on _____ .

5   My favourite date is _____ .

9 Answer the questions.

Which is your favourite month?

_____

_____

Which month don't you like?

_____

_____

When is your birthday?

_____

_____

When do you usually go on holiday?

_____

_____

GRAMMAR

1 Put in order.

usually   never   always   often   sometimes

0%   _____

        _____

        _____

        _____

100% _____

26 | *I can cook*

SOUNDS AND VOCABULARY

1 Put in three groups.

knit read drive eat ride leave sing write
see like drink type speak swim

/ɪ/: *knit* _____

_____

/iː/: *read* _____

_____

/aɪ/: *drive* _____

_____

🔊 Listen and check.

2 Say the words.

3 Complete with verbs from activity 1.

1 I can _____ a bicycle.
2 I can't _____ a car.
3 I can't _____ German newspapers.
4 I can _____ English.
5 I can't _____ poetry.
6 I can't _____ in the sea.

4 Say.

/æ/: put a tick (✓); /ə/: put a cross (✗).

1 Yes, I can.
2 I can cook.
3 Can you knit?
4 I can play the piano.
5 Can you type?

5 🔊 Listen and check.

6 Match.

Box A	Box B
play use	Japanese bicycle
speak read	letters guitar car
cook write	spaghetti chess computer
understand	Italian
drive ride	

play the guitar, _____

_____

_____

_____

_____

GRAMMAR

1 Write questions with words in *Sounds and vocabulary* activity 6.

Can you speak Japanese?
1 _____
2 _____
3 _____
4 _____
5 _____
6 _____

2 Answer the questions in activity 1 for you.

No, I can't.
1 _____
2 _____
3 _____
4 _____
5 _____
6 _____

2 Tick (✓) the correct sentence.

1   a I go out always on Saturday evening.

    b I always go out on Saturday evening.

2   a She never sees her parents.

    b Never she sees her parents.

3   a We sometimes play chess.

    b We chess play sometimes.

4   a He walks often to work.

    b He often walks to work.

5   a They usually come on Tuesday.

    b They come usually on Tuesday.

READING

1 Read and underline the adverbs of frequency.

New Year's Day is the first day of our year and is on the first of January. I usually have a party on New Year's Eve, the 31st of December. I usually invite friends to our house. We dance and eat and drink. We have a lot of fun. At midnight we always drink champagne and sing *Auld Lang Syne*. We kiss and say 'Happy New Year'.
Rachel, Birmingham

We never do anything special on New Year's Eve. We sometimes have dinner at my parents' house but we often stay at home with the children. We usually watch television. There's always a good film. We go to bed at midnight.
Bob and Mary, Cardiff

New Year's Eve is very special. I usually go to a restaurant with friends then we go to the pub. We go to Trafalgar Square and I sometimes dance in the fountain at midnight. On the first of January, I always get up in the afternoon!
Joe, London

2 Match.

	go to bed at midnight.
	goes to a restaurant.
Rachel	stay at home with their children.
Bob and Mary	invites friends to her house.
Joe	dances and has fun.
	dances in the fountain in Trafalgar Square.

3 Read and complete.

They ___*never*___ do anything

1 They _____ have dinner

   parents.

2 He _____ gets up in the

3 She _____ has a party.

4 She _____ drinks cham

5 They _____ watch telev

WRITING

1 Complete for you.

1 I sometimes _____

_____

2 I never _____

_____

3 I always _____

_____

4 I often _____

_____

5 I usually _____

_____

2 Write about what you do on a spec your country.

_____

_____

_____

_____

_____

_____

_____

_____

3 **Answer the questions.**

Do you like sightseeing?
No, I don't.

1 Do you like dancing?

_____

2 Can you play the piano?

_____

3 Are you British?

_____

4 Can your brother/sister speak English?

_____

5 Does your mother live in London?

_____

6 Has your father got a car?

_____

READING AND LISTENING

1 **Complete the conversation.**

(1) _____

No, it isn't.

(2) _____

No, I can't. But I can play the piano.

(3) _____

Yes, I have. It's in the living room.

a Have you got a piano?
b Is this your guitar?
c Can you play the guitar?

2 ▭ **Listen and check.**

3 ▭ **Listen and number.**

a What do you eat? ☐

b Yes, I can. I like cooking very much. I like Chinese food. ☐

c Do you like cooking? ☐

d Oh, good. You can cook lunch! ☐

e No, I don't. I can't cook. ☐

f I go to restaurants in the evening and I eat sandwiches for lunch. And you? Can you cook? ☐

WRITING

1 **Look at the pictures. Write sentences.**

1 _He can't sing._
2 _____
3 _____
4 _____
5 _____

2 **Write things that you _can do_ and things you _can't do._**

_____
_____
_____
_____
_____
_____
_____
_____

53

27 | *Can I have a sandwich, please?*

VOCABULARY

1 Match.

bottle   glass   piece   cup

A _____

B _____

C _____

D _____

2 Match with words in activity 1.

tea cake juice cheese bread wine coffee
pizza milk

a cup of tea, _____

_____

_____

_____

_____

3 Write your meals. What do you have for:

breakfast: *orange juice, cornflakes,* _____

_____

_____

_____

lunch: _____

_____

_____

dinner: _____

_____

_____

_____

SOUNDS

1 Circle the odd-one-out.

apple   jam   can   (can't)

1 tea cheese bread meat

2 piece wine pie ice

3 milk fruit drink fish

4 home roast bottle toma<u>to</u>

5 garlic jam apple have

2 📼 Listen and check.

3 Say the words.

4 📼 Listen and look.

Can I <u>help</u> you?

Can I have a <u>sandwich</u>?

Can I have a <u>glass</u> of <u>water</u>?

Can I have a <u>piece</u> of <u>cake</u>?

Can I have a <u>cup</u> of <u>coffee</u>?

5 📼 Listen again and repeat.

LISTENING

1 Look at the picture. Write what they eat.

Table A	Table B	Table C
a sandwich		

2 🔊 Listen and match the conversations and the tables.

Conversation 1 ☐

Conversation 2 ☐

Conversation 3 ☐

3 🔊 Listen again and complete the orders in activity 1.

READING AND WRITING

1 Complete the dialogue in a restaurant.

WAITRESS Good afternoon, can I help you?

YOU (sandwich)? _____

WAITRESS There's beef, cheese or chicken.

YOU (chicken) _____

WAITRESS Certainly. And anything to drink?

YOU (coffee) _____

WAITRESS That's a chicken sandwich and a cup of coffee. Anything else?

YOU (dessert) _____

WAITRESS There's cheesecake or apple pie with ice cream.

YOU (cheesecake) _____

WAITRESS Thank you.

2 Look at *Vocabulary* activity 3. Describe your meals.

I have breakfast at half past seven with my family. I have a glass of orange juice,

_____

_____

_____

_____

_____

28 | *Where's the station?*

VOCABULARY

1 Complete.

Across:

1 Where you can buy aspirin.
5 There is money here.
6 You put your car in a car _____ .
7 Where you can buy books.

Down:

2 Where you can buy fruit and vegetables.
3 The train stops here.
4 You can buy bread here.
6 Where you can have a drink.

2 Complete.

north   west   east   south

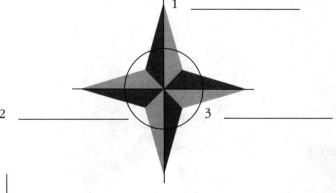

READING AND FUNCTIONS

1 Look at the map and answer.

Where's the market?
It's in Broad Street.

1 Where's the bus station?

_____

2 Where's the library?

_____

3 Where's the telephone?

_____

4 Where's the restaurant?

_____

2 Complete.

Where's the library?
It's _____ Castle Street.
_____ Castle Street?
Go _____ Oxford Road and _____ right.
It's _____ the left.

And where's the telephone?
It's _____ the car park.
_____ the car park?
Go _____ Broad Street. It's _____ the left.

3 Read and complete the map.

You are at the bus station.

a Turn left then turn right into Broad Street. Go along Broad Street. The post office is on the right.

b Turn left then turn right. Go along Broad Street. Turn left. The toilet is on the left in Church Street.

c Turn right then turn left into Oxford Road. Go along Oxford Road. The cinema is on the right.

d Turn right then turn left. Go along Oxford Road. Turn left and go along Church Street. The chemist is on your left.

e Turn right then turn left. Go straight along Oxford Road. Turn left and go along Lion Street. The bookshop is on the right.

You are in the car park.

f Turn left. Go straight along Broad Street. The bank is on the left.

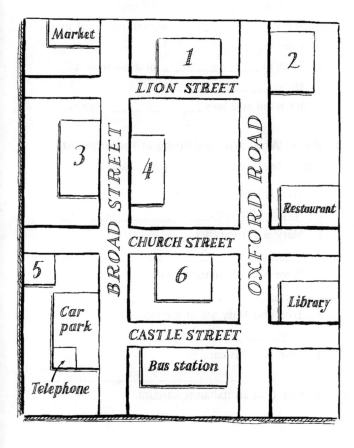

1 _____	4 _____
2 _____	5 _____
3 _____	6 _____

LISTENING

1 📼 Listen and complete.

A Excuse me, please. Where's the _____ ?

B It's in Church Street.

A And where's Church Street?

B Go _____ Castle Street. Turn _____ into Broad Street. Then turn _____ into Church Street. It's on your _____ .

A Thank you very much.

2 📼 Listen again and check.

3 📼 Listen and correct.

A Excuse me. Where's the cinema?

B It's in Broad Street.

A Where's Broad Street?

B Drive along Oxford Road for 100 metres. Turn right into Lion Street. Then turn left into Broad Street. The market is straight ahead.

A Thank you.

4 📼 Listen again and check.

SOUNDS

1 📼 Listen and look.

1 Where's the pos<u>t o</u>ffice?
2 It'<u>s i</u>n Broad Street.
3 It'<u>s o</u>n the left.
4 Wal<u>k a</u>long Church Street.
5 It's straigh<u>t a</u>head.

2 📼 Listen again and repeat.

3 Read the tour of the town. What is the name of the town?

<u>Start</u> your <u>tour</u> of <u>Bramley</u> at the <u>car</u> <u>park</u>. Go along Oak Road. Turn right into Green Street. The castle is on your right and the market is straight ahead. Turn left into Elm Street. The post office is on the left.

4 📼 Listen and underline the stressed words.

5 📼 Listen again and check.

29 | *He's buying lunch*

VOCABULARY

1 Write.

shop	*shopping*	smoke	_____
run	_____	write	_____
sit	_____	dance	_____
stop	_____	leave	_____
get	_____	have	_____
swim	_____	drive	_____
knit	_____	type	_____

2 Complete.

1   *She's writing a letter.*
2   He's _____
3   They're _____
4   He's _____
5   She's _____
6   She's _____

GRAMMAR

1 Complete.

He __*is*__ having lunch in a restaurant.
1   They _____ getting dressed.
2   She _____ watching television.
3   He _____ standing in a queue.
4   They _____ shopping.
5   She _____ buying clothes.

2 Complete.

stand   leave   dance   lie   buy   have   play

She's __*lying*__ in bed.
1   He's _____ bread from the baker.
2   They're _____ football.
3   She's _____ something to eat in a café.
4   They're _____ in a queue.
5   He's _____ in a club.
6   It's 8 am and he's _____ home.

3 Write. What are they doing at the moment?
drive   read   eat   wash   work   talk

Tom is in the bathroom.
He's washing.
1   Mary is at the office.

_____
2   Peter is in the living room.

_____
3   Tom and Mary are at the pub.

_____
4   John is in his car.

_____
5   Sam is in an Italian restaurant.

_____

58

READING AND LISTENING

1 Read the conversation below and answer the questions.

1   Where is Janet?

_____

2   Where is Paul?

_____

JANET   Hello. It's Janet. Is that you, Paul?

PAUL   Hello, Janet (1) _____

JANET   Fine. How is everyone at home?

PAUL   Very well. It's 2 o'clock here. Mum is working in the garden and Dad is walking in Hyde Park.

JANET   (2) _____

PAUL   No, she isn't in London this weekend. She's staying with a friend in Edinburgh. They're sightseeing. (3) _____

JANET   It's nine o'clock in the morning here. People are getting up and starting to go out. It's a beautiful day.

PAUL   (4) _____

JANET   Some people leave the city but many people go to Central Park. I can see the park from my flat. I can see people running and cycling and children playing basketball. In the afternoon a lot of families come to the park.

PAUL   (5) _____

JANET   I'm lying on the sofa with a cup of coffee and I'm phoning all my friends in Britain! The family I work for are walking in the park at the moment! Say hello to Mum and Dad. Bye for now, Paul.

PAUL   Bye, Janet.

2 Decide where these questions go in the conversation.

a   What time is it in New York at the moment?

b   Is Julia at home?

c   What are you doing?

d   How are you?

e   What do most New Yorkers do on Sundays?

3   [cassette] Listen and check.

4 Answer.

1   What time is it in New York?

_____

2   What time is it in London?

_____

3   What are Paul's parents doing at the moment?

_____

4   Where is Julia?

_____

5   What are many people doing in Central Park?

_____

6   What is Janet doing?

_____

WRITING

Write about what people are doing in the picture.

_____

_____

_____

_____

_____

_____

_____

_____

VOCABULARY

1 Find 20 verbs in the puzzle.

B	L	W	E	A	R	G	W
U	I	S	T	A	Y	O	A
Y	E	L	E	A	R	N	L
D	W	A	I	T	A	L	K
R	U	S	P	E	A	K	C
A	S	I	R	A	B	E	O
W	E	T	U	C	D	A	O
G	E	T	N	H	O	T	K

wear, _____

_____

_____

_____

2 Complete with verbs from activity 1.
1 Sally is _____ for the bus.
2 I am _____ English at a summer school.
3 He's _____ chicken for lunch.
4 They're _____ in a hotel.
5 She's _____ jeans.
6 They're _____ on the beach.

3 Continue the series of words.
wine jeans first daughter September
library nice Tuesday brother green at
second baker jacket clever Wednesday red
March to water

1 blue white black _____ _____
2 on in under _____ _____
3 sweater shirt shoes _____

   _____
4 chemist bookshop bank _____

   _____

5 coffee juice tea _____ _____
6 April June January _____

   _____
7 Monday Thursday Saturday _____

   _____
8 third fourth tenth _____ _____
9 quiet friendly pretty _____

   _____
10 sister son mother _____ _____

SOUNDS

1 Underline the odd-one-out.
1 leave wear eat speak
2 talk walk draw watch
3 wait stay make start
4 buy sit like lie

2 Listen and check.

3 Listen and look.
1 I'm not <u>playing</u> today.
2 She isn't <u>learning</u> <u>English</u>.
3 They aren't <u>coming</u> to the <u>party</u>.
4 He isn't <u>waiting</u> for the <u>bus</u>.
5 We aren't <u>staying</u> in a <u>hotel</u>.
6 You aren't <u>working</u> <u>today</u>.

4 Listen again and repeat.

GRAMMAR

1 Put in order and write the sentences.

1 doing what you are?

2 for we waiting taxi are a

3 coffee she making is?

4 watching not are television they

5 is he school coming not to

2 Correct the sentences.

He's watching television. (read/newspaper)
No, he isn't watching television, he's reading the newspaper.

1 He's making tea. (make/coffee)

2 They're waiting for a taxi. (wait for/bus)

3 She's getting dressed. (have/shower)

4 We're going to the cinema. (go/theatre)

5 He's talking to his brother. (talk/friend)

3 Write the questions.

he/make/lunch
Is he making lunch?

1 she/have/party

2 they/wear/jeans

3 we/go/cinema

4 you/wait/your brother

5 he/stay/hotel

LISTENING

1 🔊 Listen and complete.

MOTHER Are you getting up, Jim?
JIM Yes, (1) _____ .
What time is it?
MOTHER Half past seven. Your father (2) _____ for you.
JIM Can I have some breakfast?
MOTHER I (3) _____ coffee. And there are some cornflakes. But hurry up!
JIM OK. I (4) _____ .

2 🔊 Listen again and check.

3 🔊 Listen and underline anything different.

DAD Hello, Laura. How are you?
LAURA Fine, thanks, Dad.
DAD What are you doing at midday?
LAURA I'm having lunch with friends.
DAD What are you cooking?
LAURA Pasta and salad.
DAD Well, enjoy yourself.
LAURA Thanks. See you tomorrow.
DAD Bye.

4 🔊 Listen again and correct.

31 | *We're going to Australia*

VOCABULARY

1 Put in two groups.

week wear case plane sail meet boat
stay beach tent mountain spend city pack
sea hour visa get airport sightseeing travel

nouns: *week,* _____

_____

verbs: *wear,* _____

_____

2 Complete with words from activity 1.

1 She's going to Barcelona for one _____ .

2 She's packing her _____ .

3 She's _____ in a hotel.

4 She's going _____ in the city.

5 The _____ arrives at 7 pm and a friend
   is _____ me at the airport.

6 We're taking our _____ and we're
   camping.

7 We're going to _____ three days in the
   mountains.

8 I like lying on the _____ and swimming
   in the _____ .

GRAMMAR AND READING

1 Complete the questions.

where who when how are

1 _____ are they going for their holiday?

2 _____ are they going with?

3 _____ they staying in a hotel or _____
   they camping?

4 _____ are they leaving?

5 _____ are they travelling?

6 _____ is meeting them at the airport?

7 _____ are they getting to the airport?

8 _____ are they coming home?

2 Write questions and complete.

BILL Where (1) *are you going for your holiday?*

JANE South Africa.

BILL Wonderful! When (2) _____

JANE On Sunday. Our plane is at 3 pm.

BILL Who (3) _____

JANE A friend called Helen.

BILL How (4) _____

JANE We're going into London by bus, then we're
          taking a train to the airport.

BILL Are (5) _____

JANE Yes, we're staying in a hotel in Johannesburg
          for two nights. After that we're going to stay
          for a week with my uncle. He lives in Cape
          Town, by the sea.

BILL When (6) _____

JANE On the 2nd of March. We're staying for two
          weeks.

3 🔲 Listen and check.

**4 Write the questions in activity 2 in the 3rd
person.**

1 *Where is she going for her holiday?*

2 _____

3 _____

4 _____

5 _____

6 _____

5 Answer the questions in activity 4.

1 *She's going to South Africa.*

2 _____

3 _____

4 _____

5 _____

6 _____

6 Write your plans for the week.

Monday

I'm going to my English class on Monday morning.

1 Tuesday

_____

2 Wednesday

_____

3 Thursday

_____

4 Friday

_____

5 Saturday

_____

6 Sunday

_____

LISTENING AND WRITING

1 🔊 Listen to Phil talking to a friend about a trip to Istanbul. Tick (✓) the correct statements.

1 Phil's getting the plane from London, Heathrow on Sunday. ☐

2 He's going by train to the airport. ☐

3 He's spending a week in Istanbul. ☐

4 He's going with a friend. ☐

5 He's staying at a hotel. ☐

6 On Monday he's going to see the Blue Mosque. ☐

7 He's going on a boat on the Bosphorus on Tuesday. ☐

8 He's going to visit Topkapi Palace on Wednesday. ☐

9 He's getting a plane home on Thursday. ☐

2 🔊 Listen again and check.

3 Read Phil's postcard from Istanbul. Underline the present continuous.

Monday 11 am

Dear Jill,

<u>I'm having</u> a wonderful holiday! I'm sitting in a cafe and I'm having Turkish coffee. The Blue Mosque is very beautiful. Turkish people are very friendly. This evening we're going to a club with people from the hotel. We're staying at a good hotel near the Blue Mosque. This afternoon we're taking a taxi to Galata and tomorrow we're going shopping in the Grand Bazaar. I'm coming home on Thursday evening. Don't come to the airport, I'm driving home.

See you on Thursday evening.

Love,

Phil

4 Which sentences are about future plans? Which sentences are about something happening at the moment?

future plans: *we're going ...*

_____

something happening at the moment:
I'm having ...

5 Plan a trip to New York.

What airport are you leaving from?

When are you leaving?

Who are you going with?

Where are you staying?

What are you doing?

_____
_____
_____
_____
_____
_____
_____
_____
_____

VOCABULARY AND READING

1 Match.

film	concert hall
jazz music	theatre
play	cinema
concert	gallery
exhibition	club

2 Look at the advertisements and complete.

1 *film*   4 _____
2 _____ 5 _____
3 _____

1

THE ODEON

The Oscar-winning
The English Patient
starring Ralph Fiennes
Continues until 16 May
Mon - Fri 5.30pm, 9pm

2

The Royal Pavilion
The Ian Drake Quartet
interpret works by
Schubert and *Mozart*
MON 12 MAY 8PM £5

3

Komedia
THE GARDNER THEATRE COMPANY
present
**Do You Come
Here Often?**
A brilliant comedy
Thur 15 - Sat 17 May 8pm £10

4

THE GRANGE GALLERY
**Contemporary African Art
from Nigeria and Zimbabwe**
Dyke Road 10 May - 15 June
Mon to Sat 10 - 5pm

5

The Concorde
THE CARLA SMITH
BIG BAND
plays some of the best
contemporary jazz
Queens Road
Sat 17 May 7.45pm £8

3 Complete.

1 There's a jazz band on this evening at the
_____ .
2 _____ is on at the Odeon
until _____ .
3 There's a new play on at the
_____ .
4 There's a concert on at the
_____ on
_____ .
5 There's an African art exhibition on at the
_____ from _____
to _____ .

FUNCTIONS

1 Complete with *go* or *going*.

1 Let's _____ to the cinema this evening.
2 How about _____ to see *Hamlet* this Saturday?
3 How about _____ to the Tate Gallery this afternoon?
4 Let's _____ to see the new Ken Loach film.
5 Let's _____ out to a restaurant.
6 How about _____ to an exhibition?

2 Accept (+) or refuse (-) the suggestions in activity 1.

1 (-) I'm sorry, but I'm _going out._
2 (+) _____
3 (-) _____
4 (+) _____
5 (-) _____
6 (-) _____

3 Complete the dialogue.

A _____ going to the cinema this evening?

B _____ ?

A The new James Bond film.

B I'm sorry, but _____

A Well, _____ go to the theatre. *Hamlet* is _____ at the Aldwych.

B Yes, OK.

4 Complete with *on*, *at* or *to*.

1 What's _____?
2 Let's go _____ the theatre.
3 It's on _____ the Aldwych.
4 It starts _____ half past eight.
5 How about going to the cinema _____ Monday?

READING AND LISTENING

1 Put in order.

There's a James Bond film. ☐
Where's it on? ☐
Let's go out this evening. ☐
Yes, OK. What's on? ☐
At the Palace. ☐

2 📼 Listen and check.

3 📼 Listen and complete.

A Let's go out (1) _____ .

B I'm sorry, but I'm (2) _____ . I'm going to stay with my parents.

A Well, how about going out this (3) _____?

B Yes, OK. What's on?

A There's a T. S. Eliot (4) _____ on at the Aldwych: *The Cocktail Party*.

B I'm sorry, but I don't like the (5) _____. How about going to the (6) _____?

A Yes, OK. What's on at the Odeon?

B There's a Sylvester Stallone (7) _____ .

A I'm sorry, but I don't like Sylvester Stallone.

B Well, let's stay at home!

4 📼 Listen again and check.

WRITING

1 Write a dialogue.

A (make a suggestion) _____
B (refuse) _____
A (make another suggestion) _____
B (accept) _____

2 What's on in your town at the moment?

_____
_____
_____
_____

3 Write suggestions for things to do in the evening this week.

Monday: _How about going to a concert on Monday evening?_
Tuesday: _____
Wednesday: _____
Thursday: _____
Friday: _____
Saturday: _____
Sunday: _____

33 | *Yesterday, I was in Paris*

VOCABULARY

1 **Put in order and write eight adjectives.**

ulawf	_____	iecn	_____
mrwa	_____	yphpa	_____
eidrt	_____	dlco	_____
odrbe	_____	dnyreilf	_____

2 **Put the adjectives in two groups.**

a friendly woman   an awful match   a bored child
a happy birthday   a nice house   a tired teacher
a clever student   an unhappy man   a warm day
an ill child

positive: *friendly* _____

_____

_____

negative: *awful* _____

_____

_____

SOUNDS

1 🔊 **Listen and tick (✓) the sentence you hear.**

1 a It was a hot day.
   b It's a hot day.
2 a We were at work.
   b We're at work.
3 a She's unhappy.
   b She was unhappy.
4 a We're bored.
   b We were bored.
5 a Their friends are here.
   b Their friends were here.
6 a They were thirsty.
   b They're thirsty.

🔊 **Listen again and repeat.**

2 **Put in three groups.**

camp   sail   happy   awful   play   always   hat
bored   case   warm   plane   pack

/æ/: *camp* _____
/eɪ/: *sail* _____
/ɔ:/: *awful* _____

🔊 **Listen and check.**

GRAMMAR

1 **Write the past simple of the verb *to be*.**

I	*was*
you	_____
he/she/it	_____
we	_____
they	_____

2 **Complete with *was* or *were*.**

1 There _____ two people on the beach.
2 I _____ bored.
3 He _____ in Australia last year.
4 The film _____ awful.
5 We _____ in New York in February.
6 Their bags _____ beside them.
7 My parents _____ there yesterday.
8 It _____ very hot in the mountains.

3 **Put in two groups.**

today   yesterday   last week   this year
the last time   this week   last year

present: *today* _____

_____

past: _____

_____

4 Match the two parts of the sentences.

1 It was cold
2 They weren't cold
3 He was thirsty
4 She was in bed because
5 He was tired
6 They were bored

a it was 11.30 pm.
b she was ill.
c the film was awful.
d the window was open.
e it was a hot day.
f the bottle was empty.

READING

1 Read the passages and complete with sentences a, b and c.

a Sunday was an awful day.
b Saturday was a nice day.
c On Monday I was tired.

1 _____ It was very warm. In the morning, I was at the National Gallery with my husband. The exhibition was wonderful. I was at home for lunch. In the afternoon, I was tired but there was a good film on television so I wasn't bored.

2 _____ I was at the office from eight o'clock to half past twelve. There were a lot of people to see and a lot of letters to write. In the afternoon, I was at a meeting with my boss. In the evening, I was on a busy train home for one hour. The shops were closed and there was no food in the fridge. My wife was late home from work. Her day was very busy, too!

3 _____ It was cold. I was unhappy because my boyfriend was away. He was in London for the week. All my friends were busy and my parents were on holiday. My car was at the garage. My dinner was awful and after it I was ill.

2 Decide if the writers are men or women.

3 Complete.

1 a It was a _____ day.
b The exhibition was _____ .
c There was a _____ film on television.
2 a The train was _____ .
b The shops were _____ .
c It was an _____ day.
3 a My friends were _____ .
b My dinner was _____ .

WRITING

1 Complete for you.

1 Yesterday I _____

2 Last night I _____

3 Today I _____

4 The last time I _____

5 Last year I _____

6 This year I _____

2 Write about last week for you.

_____
_____
_____
_____
_____
_____
_____
_____

VOCABULARY

1 Tick (✓) the words in the story in the Student's Book.

sea murder hungry mountain Miss plane
butler wine theatre murderer outback
colonel Mrs cinema scream detective guitar
professor party dead concert sergeant
beach Lady exhibition

2 Complete with these words.

alone anyone awful everything hungry
knife something thirsty

1 He was a good butler but he was an
   _____ cook.

2 They were _____ but there wasn't
   any wine.

3 Yesterday, it was warm and _____
   was fine.

4 Was she _____ in the kitchen?

5 There was a _____ on the table.

6 Was there _____ in the dining room?

7 They were _____ but there wasn't
   any food.

8 Was there _____ on the table?

GRAMMAR

1 Complete with *was* or *were*.

   Was he in the kitchen?

1 _____ there many people at the exhibition
   yesterday.

2 _____ he at school with you?

3 _____ they in England in August?

4 _____ she ill last night?

5 _____ there any food at the party?

6 _____ you tired last night?

2 Match these answers with the questions in activity 1.

a Yes, they were. ☐

b No, there wasn't. ☐

c No, she wasn't. ☐

d Yes, he was. ☐

e Yes, I was. ☐

f Yes, there were. ☐

3 Write questions.

   Was it a warm day?

   No, it was a cold day.

1 _____

   No, the food was awful.

2 _____

   Yes, they were very friendly.

3 _____

   There was only a knife on the table.

4 _____

   No, he was in the living room.

5 _____

   No, there was only water and orange juice.

6 _____

   No, she wasn't alone. Her mother was with her.

4 Write with an object pronoun.

me you him her it us them

   I was with *John* at the cinema last night.
   I was with him at the cinema yesterday.

1 Please come to the theatre with *John and me.*

   _____

2 Peter was in the kitchen with *Jane* this morning.

   _____

3 I was at home with *my brothers.*

   _____

4 There was a letter in *my bag.*

   _____

5 Write two short answers.

Was she at home on Saturday?

Yes, she was.

No, she wasn't.

1 Were they in the dining room?

_____

_____

2 Are you happy today?

_____

_____

3 Does he like swimming?

_____

_____

4 Is the food good?

_____

_____

5 Was there any wine on the table?

_____

_____

6 Is he a good cook?

_____

_____

7 Are they coming to the party?

_____

_____

8 Was he in the garden?

_____

_____

LISTENING

1 Listen and match.

2 Listen again and tick the correct sentences.

1 Mr Schmitt was tall, dark and good-looking. ☐

2 He was a good teacher. ☐

3 He was good fun. ☐

4 Mrs Chamoux was tall and fair. ☐

5 She was a good teacher. ☐

6 She was very clever. ☐

7 Mr James was short and fair. ☐

8 His English wasn't very good. ☐

9 He wasn't very friendly. ☐

WRITING

What was your English teacher like at school?

_____

_____

_____

_____

_____

A ☐   **B** ☐   **C** ☐   69

35 | *They didn't have any computers*

VOCABULARY

1 Match and write words.

Box A	Box B
video personal	cleaner machine
fax vacuum washing	stereo recorder

video recorder
_____
_____

2 Tick (✓) for you.

1 I had a bicycle when I was a child. ☐

2 I had a computer before I had a television. ☐

3 I've got a personal stereo. ☐

4 I haven't got a fax machine. ☐

5 There is a vacuum cleaner in my house. ☐

6 I had a washing machine before I had a dishwasher. ☐

3 Complete.

I had *a video recorder* when I was a child.

1 I had _____ when I was a child.

2 I had _____ when I was a child.

3 I had _____ when I was a child.

4 I had _____ when I was a child.

4 Write and say. Where were the things in activity 3 in your house?

The video recorder was in the living room.

1 _____
_____

2 _____
_____

3 _____
_____

4 _____
_____

SOUNDS

1 🔲 Listen and look.

1 They <u>didn't</u> <u>have</u> a <u>telephone</u>.

2 We <u>had</u> a <u>vacuum</u> <u>cleaner</u>.

3 My <u>parents</u> had a <u>car</u>.

4 I <u>didn't</u> <u>have</u> a <u>computer</u>.

5 She <u>had</u> a <u>dishwasher</u>.

2 🔲 Listen again and repeat.

3 🔲 Listen and underline the stressed syllables in these words from Lesson 35.

coffee   tobacco   potatoes   sandwich   cameras machine   engine   newspaper   gunpowder recorder

4 🔲 Listen again and repeat.

GRAMMAR

1 Complete with *have* or *had*.

1 We _____ a television in every room of the house.

2 My parents didn't _____ a car when I was a child.

3 Did she _____ a fax machine in her office?

4 She _____ a telephone in the hall.

5 We didn't _____ any money.

6 Did you _____ computers at school?

7 I _____ a radio before I _____ a television.

8 She didn't _____ a video recorder when I was at her house.

2 Put in order.

1 have television I not a did

_____

2 dishwasher child when had we was a a I

_____

3 computer was at there a school my

_____

4 have you holiday did good a?

_____

5 lunch I for sandwich had a

_____

3 Write and say what they had and didn't have in these years.

In 1900, *they didn't have planes but they had steam engines.*

In 1920, _____

_____

In 1940, _____

_____

In 1960, _____

_____

In 1980, _____

_____

In 1990, _____

_____

4 Write questions.

Did you have a computer?

No, I didn't have a computer.

1 _____

Yes, my parents had a car.

2 _____

Yes, the radio programmes were very good.

3 _____

Yes, we had a black and white television.

4 _____

No, we didn't have a dishwasher when I was a child.

5 _____

No, there weren't any computers in my school.

READING AND WRITING

1 Match questions and answers. There are two extra answers.

1 Did you have a bicycle when you were a child?

2 What was your family's first car?

3 Did you have a computer when you were at school?

4 Was there a dishwasher at your home when you were a child?

5 When did you have your first computer?

a No. No one had computers when I was at school.

b When I was sixteen. I had an Amstrad. It was a birthday present.

c Yes, I had my first bicycle when I was eight. It was a beautiful bicycle. It was blue and red. I was very happy.

d Yes, we had a television when I was a child but it was in black and white not in colour.

e No, I haven't got a fax machine.

f No. We didn't have a dishwasher but we had a washing machine.

g Our first car was an Austin Mini. It was very small and we were a very big family!

2 Write the questions for the two extra answers.

1 _____

2 _____

3 Answer the questions in activity 1 for you.

1 _____

_____

2 _____

_____

3 _____

_____

4 _____

_____

5 _____

_____

VOCABULARY

1 Complete with *this* or *last*.

1 I have a lot of work to do _____ month.

2 I played tennis with a friend _____ week.

3 _____ month was March.

4 We visited Italy _____ year.

5 The weather is beautiful _____ morning.

6 He isn't working _____ week because he's ill.

2 Put a tick (✓) by the sentences in the past simple.

1 I work four hours a day on my computer. ☐

2 She walks to work every morning. ☐

3 We played cards on Saturday evenings. ☐

4 We had lunch in the garden in summer. ☐

5 He cooks the family meals at the weekend. ☐

6 They liked to go dancing on Friday evenings. ☐

7 I like to travel a lot. ☐

8 We listened to a play on the radio. ☐

READING

1 Read and underline the verbs in the past simple.

2 Read and say how many nights they stayed in each place.

Venice: _____

Florence: _____

The Abruzzes mountains: _____

Rome: _____

3 Complete.

1 They camped in _____ _____ .

2 They hired a car in _____ .

3 They visited art galleries in _____ .

4 They stayed in a small hotel in _____ .

5 They walked in _____ _____ .

6 They had a wonderful meal in a restaurant in _____ .

GRAMMAR

1 Write the past form of these verbs.

listen	*listened*	play	_____
walk	_____	visit	_____
watch	_____	have	_____
cook	_____	live	_____
stay	_____	be	_____
start	_____	finish	_____
travel	_____	work	_____

Last month we had a holiday in Italy. We travelled around the country for fourteen days. We travelled to Milan by plane and we hired a car there. First we visited Venice. We stayed in a small hotel for four nights. Then we visited Florence. We liked Florence very much so we decided to stay there for three nights and visit the art galleries. After Florence, we camped in the Abruzzes mountains near Rome for two nights. We walked in the mountains and cooked our meals on a camp fire. We finished our tour in Rome which is my favourite city. We stayed for five nights in a hotel in the city centre. On our last night we had a wonderful meal in a restaurant. We travelled back to Britain by plane from Rome. It was a marvellous holiday!

2 Complete with a verb in the past.

1 I _____ work when I
_____ eighteen.

2 When I _____ in London, I
_____ in a bank.

3 When I _____ a child, I
_____ football in the school team.

4 My mother _____ work at eight
o'clock and _____ work at five
o'clock.

5 I _____ at home yesterday.

6 There _____ a good film on last
night so we _____ television until
midnight.

3 Write sentences in the past with five verbs from
activity 1.

1 _____
2 _____
3 _____
4 _____
5 _____

4 Complete with a preposition.

at   in   on   to   until   from

1 I lived _____ London when I was a child.

2 He works _____ 9 am _____ 5 pm.

3 She was _____ university _____ 1989.

4 We played tennis _____ eight o'clock.

5 I cook dinner _____ Sundays.

6 I finished work _____ six o'clock.

5 Continue for you.

1 Last year I _____

2 When I was a child my parents _____

3 When I lived _____

4 At weekends _____

5 Yesterday I _____

6 Last week _____

WRITING

Look at the pictures and write about John's
Sunday.

SOUNDS

1 🔊 Listen and underline the word with a different sounding ending.

1   wanted   finished   started   painted
2   died   lived   played   worked
3   watched   arrived   stopped   liked
4   opened   listened   visited   changed

2 🔊 Put a tick (✓) if you can hear the underlined *t*.

1   She didn't die in Spain.
2   He didn't invite his friend last night.
3   We didn't travel by train.
4   He didn't start until he was ten.
5   She didn't have a big breakfast.
6   We didn't do anything yesterday.

3 🔊 Listen again and repeat.

GRAMMAR

1   Put in order.
1   ten started yesterday at she work
    _____
2   London live he to in want didn't
    _____
3   1881 in born Malaga Picasso in was
    _____
4   years Bangkok lived in three we for
    _____
5   last watch they night television didn't
    _____
6   when was he paint ten he to started
    _____

2   Are the sentences in the past simple or the present simple? Complete with *don't/doesn't* or *didn't*.
1   No, thank you. I _____ want any tea, I _____ like it.
2   He _____ go to Istanbul last year.
3   She _____ work at the travel agency now.
4   We _____ visit the Louvre when we were in Paris.
5   I _____ like rap music.
6   He _____ start teaching until he was thirty.

3   Write in the negative.
1   We lived in Italy for three years.
    _____
2   She worked in a bank.
    _____
3   He studied at Barcelona University.
    _____
4   Picasso painted the *Mona Lisa*.
    _____
5   He died in 1975.
    _____
6   He returned to Spain to live.
    _____

4   Write five things that you wanted to do last year but you didn't do.
    I didn't visit the USA.
    _____
    _____
    _____
    _____
    _____

READING

1 Read and match the descriptions with the famous people in the pictures. There is one extra picture.

1 She was born in Warsaw in Poland in 1867. She married a Frenchman in 1898 and lived in France until she died in 1934. She worked with her husband Pierre. She was also the first woman to teach at the Sorbonne in Paris. She received the Nobel Prize in 1903 and again in 1911.

2 He was born in Ulm in Germany in 1872. In 1896 he went to study in Zürich. In 1900 he changed his nationality and he became a Swiss citizen and from 1902 he worked in Berne. He changed his nationality again in 1940 when he became an American citizen. He received the Nobel Prize in 1921. He died in Princeton, USA in 1955.

3 This famous Spaniard was born in Figueras in 1904. He studied at the Fine Arts Academy in Madrid from 1921 to 1925. He lived and worked in Paris from 1927 to 1938. In 1940 he travelled to the United States. He returned to live in Spain until he died in 1989.

Salvador Dali

Marie Curie

Albert Einstein

Margaret Thatcher

2 Complete with a suitable verb.

1 Marie Curie _____ a teacher at the Sorbonne.

2 Albert Einstein _____ the Nobel Prize in 1921.

3 Dali _____ art in Madrid.

4 Einstein first _____ his nationality in 1900.

5 Marie Curie _____ Pierre in 1898.

6 Dali _____ in 1989.

3 Correct these false statements.

Marie Curie was born in Paris.
She wasn't born in Paris. She was born in Warsaw.

1 She worked with her brother.

_____

_____

2 Einstein studied in Berne.

_____

_____

3 He received the Nobel Prize in 1911.

_____

_____

4 Dali lived in Paris until 1927.

_____

_____

5 He lived in Paris until he died in 1989.

_____

_____

WRITING

Write a few sentences about the life of Margaret Thatcher. Use this information.

Year of birth 1925; chemistry at Oxford University; first British woman prime minister; prime minister 1979–90

_____

_____

_____

_____

_____

38 | *Did you take a photograph?*

SOUNDS AND VOCABULARY

1 Underline the stressed syllable.

recognise   appear   happen   realise   disappear
follow   decide   return

2 🔲 Listen and check. Say the words aloud.

3 Match.

1 Did you wait   a fine?
2 Did she help   b the dog back to the village?
3 Did they walk   c any photographs?
4 Was the weather   d at the hotel?
5 Did you stay   e for a long time?
6 Did you take   f you?
7 Did they follow   g to the village?

4 🔲 Listen and repeat the sentences in activity 3.

5 Underline the odd-one-out.

1 dark   walk   bark   start
2 black   back   call   cat
3 wait   stay   take   last
4 cold   fog   lots   lost
5 climb   find   still   time

6 🔲 Listen and check.

7 Complete with a word from each series in activity 5.

1 It was very cold and _____ outside.
2 Did she _____ you last night?
3 Did you _____ for a long time?
4 There were _____ of birds.
5 They looked for the cat everywhere but they
   didn't _____ it.

GRAMMAR

1 Complete with *did* or *do/does*.

1 _____ you wait for a long time?
2 _____ you arrive back before the
   children?
3 _____ he still live in Vienna?
4 _____ they get lost when they walked
   back?
5 _____ you usually go out on Saturday
   evenings?
6 _____ she find her cat?

2 Answer the questions for you.

Did you go to work yesterday? *Yes, I did.*

1 Did you clean the house yesterday?

   _____

2 Did you see friends last weekend?

   _____

3 Did you go for a walk on Sunday?

   _____

4 Did you go shopping last week?

   _____

3 Write questions.

Did you go to the cinema last night?
Yes, I did.

1 _____
   No, we didn't.

2 _____
   Yes, she was.

3 _____
   No, I didn't.

4 _____
   No, they didn't.

5 _____
   Yes, he did.

4 Write four questions you can ask your friend about what he/she did last weekend.

Did you revise your English last weekend?

_____

_____

_____

_____

READING AND LISTENING

1 Look at the pictures and write words or expressions you can use to describe them.

dog snake

_____

_____

_____

_____

_____

2 Read story A and match it with one of the pictures.

A

Candy Steele was four years old when her dog, Jet, saved her life. There was a swimming pool in the Steele family's garden. One morning, when her mother was in the kitchen, Candy fell into the swimming pool. She started to call for help. Jet barked at the kitchen door until Mrs Steele opened it and ran outside to help Candy.

3 Underline the verbs in the past simple.

4 Listen to an interview with Candy's mother. Underline anything in the passage that is different.

5 Separate the two animal stories below.

B

Sean Bailey and his nine-year-old sister were in their garden when a dangerous snake appeared ...

_____

_____

_____

_____

_____

_____

C

Harvey, a five-year-old Persian cat, climbed into a washing machine and went to sleep ...

_____

_____

_____

_____

_____

... The children were very frightened and they shouted for help. His owner, Mrs Dickens, closed the door and started the machine. Their dog, Leo, saved their lives. He stayed ten minutes in the machine before Mrs Dickens noticed him through the glass door. He jumped in front of them and barked at the snake until it disappeared behind a tree. She stopped the machine and pulled a very clean cat out. He didn't sleep in the washing machine again! The snake bit the dog and he died.

39 | *We went to New York!*

VOCABULARY

1 Complete.

Across:

1 You show this at the frontier when you visit another country.

6 You look at this to find the times of buses and trains.

8 You can pay with this.

Down:

2 You can see them on the wall outside the cinema or the theatre.

3 You buy one to go into the cinema or the theatre.

4 When you buy something the shop assistant gives you one.

5 You can look at this when you are choosing a place to go on holiday.

7 You pay this when you go to a restaurant, for example.

2 Match the nouns and verbs.

pay	money
spend	photograph
look at	bill
take	timetable
stay	hotel
have	dinner

3 Write sentences with the words in activity 2.

1 *I didn't pay the bill.*

2 _____

3 _____

4 _____

5 _____

6 _____

7 _____

8 _____

GRAMMAR

1 Complete with a question word.

1 _____ did you go for your holiday last summer?

2 _____ did you stay there?

3 _____ did you do in the evenings?

4 _____ did you go with?

5 _____ did you travel there?

6 _____ did you spend on entertainment?

2 Answer the questions in activity 1.

1 _____
2 _____
3 _____
4 _____
5 _____
6 _____

3 Write the past simple of these verbs.

buy	_____	find	_____
fly	_____	get	_____
leave	_____	do	_____
see	_____	spend	_____
give	_____	go	_____
come	_____	take	_____

4 Complete with a verb from activity 3.

1 I _____ some bread and cheese from the supermarket.
2 They _____ to the hotel at half past six.
3 The journey _____ two hours.
4 She _____ from Kennedy Airport to Heathrow.
5 I _____ a good film on television last night.
6 We _____ to the theatre last Saturday.

5 Write sentences in the past simple with the extra verbs in activity 3.

1 _____
2 _____
3 _____
4 _____
5 _____
6 _____

LISTENING

1 🔊 Listen to Sue and Cathy talking about a trip to Paris. Number the questions.

a   How did you get to Paris? ☐
b   Did you enjoy your trip to Paris? ☐
c   Did you go out in the evenings? ☐
d   Did you go up the Eiffel Tower? ☐
e   Did you buy anything? ☐
f   How long did you go for? ☐

2 🔊 Listen again and tick (✓) the true statements.

1   Cathy enjoyed her trip to Paris. ☐
2   She stayed there for a week. ☐
3   The weather was very good. ☐
4   She flew from Heathrow. ☐
5   She didn't go up the Eiffel Tower. ☐
6   She didn't buy anything. ☐

3 Correct the false statements in activity 2.

_____
_____
_____
_____

WRITING

Describe a trip you made to a town. Use the questions in *Listening* activity 1 to help you.

_____
_____
_____
_____
_____
_____
_____
_____

VOCABULARY

1 Underline the adjectives.

beach bill garden peaceful kitchen dark timetable noise gallery beautiful platform foggy bird village dirty mountain clever railway station weather country thirsty flowers quiet dream journey receipt wonderful hungry credit card

2 Match these definitions with a noun from activity 1.

1 Where you go if you want to take the train.

2 Something you can have when you are asleep.

3 You find them in the garden.

4 It can fly but it's not a plane.

5 A very small town.

6 The waiter gives you this at the end of your meal.

7 You can use this to pay for something.

8 A place where you can see art exhibitions.

3 Complete with an adjective from activity 1.

1 I drank some water because I was very

   _____ .

2 The weather isn't very good today. It's cold and

   _____ .

3 Go and have a wash, you're very _____ !

4 There is no noise in the garden, it's very

   _____ .

5 We had a _____ time in Paris.

GRAMMAR

1 Decide what tense it is.

present simple: _____

present continuous: _____

past simple: _____

1 I'm living in a flat in Brighton with a friend.

2 She didn't want to go to the exhibition.

3 What do you usually do in the evenings?

4 They took a taxi to the station.

5 We're studying economics this year.

6 I read that book when I was at school.

7 Do you still work in the clothes shop in the high street?

8 I'm afraid I don't know where they live.

9 He made a wonderful meal last night.

10 They're watching a football match on television.

2 Underline the verbs in the past simple.

buy spent take had arrived go left make run wrote get are gave see wore say heard happen was knew think brought sell flew eat do came find drank met

3 Write the past simple of the verbs in the present in activity 2.

bought _____

_____

_____

4 Complete with a verb from activity 2.

1 We _____ from Heathrow airport to New York.

2 She _____ a bottle of perfume and some cigarettes in the duty-free shop.

3 When did you _____ home?

4 We _____ to Rome for the weekend.

5 We _____ an interesting modern art exhibition at the Tate Gallery.

6 The journey only _____ two hours.

7 He _____ lunch at a restaurant with a friend.

8 Shakespeare _____ *Hamlet.*

9 I _____ John for the first time at my parents' house.

10 The waiter _____ me the bill at the end of the meal.

5 Write four more sentences in the past simple with verbs from activity 2.

1 _____
2 _____
3 _____
4 _____

6 Match.

1 Do you like sightseeing? a No, I didn't.
2 Have you got a dog b Yes, they are.
3 Was it foggy yesterday? c Yes, I do.
4 Did they go out last night? d No, I haven't.
5 Are they coming tomorrow? e Yes, she does.
6 Does she still work there? f No, there isn't.
7 Did you meet her? g Yes, it was.
8 Is there a garage? h No, they didn't.

7 Write.

A *He's climbing a mountain.*

B _____

C _____

D _____

E _____

F _____

8 Write sentences for you.

1 I never _____
2 I sometimes _____
3 I usually _____
4 I often _____
5 I always _____

SOUNDS

1 How do you pronounce the letter *a*? Put the words into two groups.

start take stay car came bark game
father wait can't day aren't card play

/ɑː/: _____

/eɪ/: _____

2 Listen and check. Say the words.

3 How do you pronounce the letter *o*? Put the words into two groups.

stop close smoke got orange sorry
moment office shop hotel bottle those

/ɒ/: _____

/əʊ/: _____

4 Listen and check. Say the words.

5 Underline the stressed syllables.

passenger photograph exhibition country
disappear platform unhappy September
afternoon

6 Listen and check. Say the words.

Tapescripts

Lesson 1 Listening and writing, activity 1

A What's your name, please?
B I'm Petra.
A Hello, Petra.
B And what's your name?
A I'm Maria.
b Goodbye.

Lesson 1 Listening and writing, activity 2

Conversation 1
KATY Hello. What's your name?
STEVE My name's Steve. And what's your name?
KATY My name's Katy.

Conversation 2
JANE Hello. What's your name?
ANNA My name's Anna. And what's your name?
JANE My name's Jane.

Lesson 2 Listening and speaking, activity 1

Conversation 1
BILL Hello, I'm Bill. What's your name?
PAT Hello, Bill. I'm Pat.
BILL What's your job, Pat?
PAT I'm an engineer.

Conversation 2
CATHY Hello, I'm Cathy. What's your name?
ERIC Hello, Cathy. I'm Eric.
CATHY What's your job, Eric?
ERIC I'm a journalist.

Lesson 2 Listening and speaking, activity 3

JOHN Hello. I'm John. What's your name?
JOHN And what's your job?

Lesson 3 Sounds, activity 2

six three nine one five eight ten
four two seven

Lesson 3 Listening and speaking, activity 2

Conversation 1
PHIL What's your phone number, Sarah?
SARAH 01789 492 873.

Conversation 2
BILL Jeanne, what's your telephone number?
JEANNE 01295 906 725.

Conversation 3
CHRIS What's your phone number, Tom?
TOM 01692 594 829.

Conversation 4
JILL Ben, what's your telephone number?
BEN 01580 731 426.

Lesson 3 Listening and speaking, activity 4

Conversation 1
JOHN Hello, Emma. How are you?
EMMA I'm fine. What's your phone number, John?
JOHN 01794 320 491

Conversation 2
MEG Hello. I'm Meg. I'm a student. What's your name?
JIM Hello, Meg. I'm Jim. I'm a student, too.
MEG What's your phone number.
JIM 01246 790 784.

Lesson 4 Vocabulary and sounds, activity 3

1 name 2 what 3 please 4 hello
5 seven 6 are

Lesson 4 Reading and listening, activity 1

HELEN Are you Philip?
PHILIP Yes, I am. Are you Jane?
HELEN No, I'm not.
PHILIP What's your name?
HELEN My name's Helen.
PHILIP What's your job?
HELEN I'm a doctor.

Lesson 4 Reading and listening, activity 2

A Are you a journalist?
B Yes, I am. And you, are you a doctor?
A No, I'm not. I'm a teacher.

Lesson 4 Reading and listening, activity 3

A Hello. Are you Steve?
B No, I'm not. I'm Michael.
A And what's your name, please?
C My name's Naomi.
A Thank you.

Lesson 5 Listening and speaking, activity 2

SAMMY Hello. I'm Sammy.
JANET Hello, Sammy. My name's Janet.
SAMMY Are you American, Janet?
JANET No, I'm from Canada. And you? Are you British?
SAMMY Yes, I am. I'm from London.

Lesson 5 Listening and speaking, activity 3

1 What's your name?
2 Are you American?
3 Where are you from?
4 What's your job?

Lesson 6 Vocabulary and sounds, activity 1

thirteen twenty twelve five fifteen
eleven eighteen nine two seventeen

Lesson 6 Reading and listening, activity 2

1 Mayumi is from Tokyo. She's Japanese. She's a teacher. She isn't married.
2 Eric is a student in Paris. He isn't French. He's British. He's from Cambridge in England. He's married.
3 Jorge is a taxi driver. He isn't married. He's from São Paulo in Brazil.
4 Amina is Indian. She's from Bombay. She's a doctor in London. She isn't married.

Lesson 7 Vocabulary and sounds, activity 1

you   two
your   four
job   from
country   number
phone   no

Lesson 7 Listening and writing, activity 2

1 She's a tennis player. She's twenty-eight years old. She's German and she's from Mannheim. She isn't married.
2 He's an actor. He's American and he's from Los Angeles. He's thirty-seven years old. He isn't married.

Lesson 8 Listening and writing, activity 1

Conversation 1
Q Are you American, John?
JOHN No, I'm British. I'm from London.
Q And what's your job?
JOHN I'm a hairdresser.
Q Who's your favourite singer?
JOHN David Bowie.

Conversation 2
Q What's your nationality Maria?
MARIA I'm Italian.
Q Where are you from in Italy?
MARIA I'm from Venice.
Q And what's your job?
MARIA I'm a journalist.
Q Who's your favourite singer?
MARIA Pavarotti.

Conversation 3
Q Where are you from, Sam?
SAM New York.
Q Are you American?
SAM Yes, I am.
Q What's your job?
SAM I'm a taxi driver.
Q Who's your favourite singer?
SAM Phil Collins.

Lesson 9 Vocabulary and listening, activity 4

Conversation 1
Q How old are you, Amy?
AMY I'm 19.
Q And how old are your brothers and sisters?
AMY My sister Sally is 19, too. We're twins. My brother Sam is 22 and my other brother Teddy is 15. Janet, my other sister, is 29.

Conversation 2
Q How old are you, John?
JOHN I'm 28.
Q How old are your brothers and sisters?
JOHN My twin brothers, Tom and Dick, are 13. My sister Julia is 17 and my other sister Emma is 12.

Lesson 10 Sounds, activity 1

wallets umbrellas cassettes clocks sandwiches watches pens numbers buses keys

Lesson 10 Sounds, activity 2

1 What's this?
2 What's that?
3 What are these?
4 Who's this?

Lesson 10 Reading and listening, activity 2

Conversation 1
A What are these?
B They're cassettes.
A Are they your cassettes?
B No, they aren't.

Conversation 2
A Are those your books?
B Yes, they are.
A Is this your dictionary?
B No, it isn't.

Conversation 3
A What's this?
B It's my car key.
A And what's that?
B I don't know. It isn't my key.

Conversation 4
A Who are they?
B They're Anne and George. They're my neighbours.
A Are they married?
B No! They're brother and sister!

Lesson 11 Listening, activity 1

CUSTOMER How much are these videos?
ASSISTANT They're £12.30.
CUSTOMER And how much are the cassettes?
ASSISTANT They're £9.99.

Lesson 11 Listening, activity 2

CUSTOMER How much is the pizza, please?
ASSISTANT It's £2.45.
CUSTOMER And how much are the sandwiches?
ASSISTANT They're 89 pence.

Lesson 11 Listening, activity 3

CUSTOMER How much is this blue skirt, please?
ASSISTANT It's £35.
CUSTOMER And how much is that green jacket?
ASSISTANT It's £62.

Lesson 12 Listening, activity 2

Conversation 1
A Excuse me. Is my brother Enrico here, please?
B Is he a student?
A Yes, he is.
B What's his name?
A Amado. Enrico Amado.
B How do you spell that?
A A-M-A-D-O
B Oh yes. He's in Simon Smith's class.

Conversation 2
C Excuse me. Is my bag here, please?
D Is this your bag?
C No, it isn't.
D What's in your bag?
C A book, my wallet, my keys and two pens.
D Is this it?
C Yes, it is. Thank you very much.

Conversation 3
E Are these your cassettes?
F What are they?
E Oasis and U2.
F No, they aren't. They're my sister's cassettes.
E Where is she?
F At work.

Lesson 13 Listening

Conversation 1
A Is that your son?
B No, it isn't. It's my neighbour's son.
A Have you got any children?
B No, I haven't. I'm not married.

Conversation 2
A Is this your car?
B No it isn't. It's my sister's car. Have you got a car?
A Yes, I have. It's a Rover.
B Where is it?
A It's in the car park.

Conversation 3
A How old are you?
B I'm nineteen.
A Have you got any brothers and sisters?
B Yes, I've got two brothers and one sister.
A How old are they?
B 17, 15 and 12.
A What are their names?
B Mark, Carl and Jessica.

Lesson 15 Reading and listening, activity 2

A
Ladies and gentlemen the plane is ready for take off.
Put your bags in the hand luggage compartment.
Please sit down and fasten your seat belts.
Don't smoke and don't use mobile telephones or computers.

B
A Sit down. John, close the door, please. Thank you.
B What lesson is it today, Mr James?
A Lesson 16. Open your books at page 43. Do activities 3 and 5.
B What about number 4?
A No, don't do that. Greg Smith! Don't listen to your personal stereo in class! Put it in your bag!

C
CLAIRE Hello, Jane. How are you?
JANE Hello, Claire. I'm fine. And you, how is the family?
CLAIRE We're all very well. But don't stand outside. Come in and have a cup of tea.
JANE Thanks.
CLAIRE Take your coat off. Sit down. Would you like coffee or tea?
JANE Tea, please.
CLAIRE Have some cake. It's chocolate and orange.
JANE Thank you very much.

Lesson 18 Sounds, activity 1

two syllables: today morning Wednesday breakfast birthday shopping
three syllables: afternoon cinema radio Saturday

Lesson 19 Listening and speaking, activity 2

SYLVIE Do you like beer, Mike?
MIKE Yes, I do. I like beer very much.
SYLVIE And do you like tea?
MIKE No, I don't.

Lesson 19 Listening and speaking, activity 3

1 Do you like football?
2 Do you like beer?
3 Do you like chocolate?
4 Do you like fish?
5 Do you like burgers?

Lesson 20 Vocabulary and sounds, activity 2

3.15 12.45 6.30 8.15 3.45 9.30

Lesson 20 Listening, activity 1

A What time do you have breakfast, Maggie?
B At half past seven. I have breakfast with my family. I leave home at a quarter past eight.
A When do you arrive at work?
B At a quarter to nine. I have a cup of coffee with a friend and I start work at nine o'clock.
A Do you go home for lunch?
B Yes, I have lunch at half past twelve with my sister. We have a sandwich and fruit juice.
A When do you finish work in the evening?
B At half past five. I arrive home at six o'clock and I have a cup of tea.

Lesson 21 Sounds, activity 2

train	day
time	like
bus	does
leave	read
boat	don't
car	start

Lesson 21 Reading and listening, activity 2

MARY Hello. My name's Mary. I work at a language school. Are you a student?

KEVIN Hello, Mary. No, I'm not a student. I'm a teacher. My name's Kevin.

MARY Where do you work?

KEVIN At the International School in London.

MARY Do you live in London?

KEVIN No, I live with my brother in Bath.

MARY When do you work?

KEVIN I work on Monday, Tuesday, Wednesday and Friday. I start work at half past nine in the morning.

MARY When do you leave home in the morning?

KEVIN I leave home at a quarter past seven. I go to London by train.

MARY When does your train leave?

KEVIN It leaves at a quarter to eight and it arrives in London at a quarter to nine.

MARY And when do you finish work and go home?

KEVIN I finish work at a quarter to four. And I arrive home at half past six.

MARY What do you do on Thursday?

KEVIN I have breakfast in bed at eleven o'clock!

Lesson 22 Vocabulary and listening, activity 2

JOHN Breakfast. I don't eat much for lunch but I have a big breakfast. It's my favourite meal. To start the day, at half past seven, I have a cup of tea in bed. Then at 8.00 I have breakfast. I drink two cups of black coffee. I have a bowl of muesli and milk then I eat an egg and toast with jam.

Lesson 22 Vocabulary and listening, activity 4

HELEN My favourite meal is lunch. I don't eat much breakfast so I have a big lunch. I like meat – chicken and steak – and I like French fries, pasta or beans. I don't like vegetables, but I eat fruit. I usually drink beer or water with my lunch. I don't drink wine.

Lesson 23 Listening, activity 2

Mike

Q Do you like going shopping, Mike?

MIKE I like going shopping for clothes but not for food. I don't like going to the supermarket.

Q What about your job? Do you like that?

MIKE No. I'm an engineering student and I don't like working!

Q And what do you like doing on holiday? Where do you go?

MIKE I go to Spain. I like lying on the beach and listening to rock music on my personal stereo.

Q Do you go sightseeing?

MIKE No, I don't like walking so I don't go sightseeing and I don't like writing postcards. I really like dancing so I go to nightclubs in the evening.

Karen

Q What do you like doing, Karen?

KAREN My favourite activity is reading. I haven't got a television so I read in the evenings. I don't like watching television at all. I like shopping for clothes. I go on Saturdays with a friend. But I don't like food shopping.

Q What about your job? Do you like that?

KAREN Yes. I'm a teacher and I like going to work.

Q And what do you like doing on holiday? Where do you go?

KAREN I love skiing so I go to the Alps in January or February.

Q And in July and August? Do you go away?

KAREN Yes. I visit different countries. I go with friends. I like sightseeing and eating in foreign restaurants.

Q Do you write postcards?

KAREN No, never. I don't like writing postcards.

Lesson 24 Listening, activity 1

A Crook's Holiday Homes. Good morning.

B Hello. My name's Fiona Rogers. Have you got holiday flats in Spain, please?

A Where exactly in Spain?

B On the Riviera.

A Yes. We've got holiday flats in Alicante. They're by the sea. Is it for a family?

B Yes, a family of four.

A That's fine. We've got a flat with one bedroom, a bathroom and a kitchen. There are two beds in the bedroom and there's a sofa-bed in the living room.

B Is there a washing machine?

A Yes. It's in the kitchen, and there's a fridge and a gas cooker.

B Is there a telephone?

A No, there isn't.

B Is there a balcony?

A Yes, with a table and four chairs.

B That's fine. How much is the flat for a week in July?

A £250.

B Thank you. Goodbye.

A Goodbye.

Lesson 25 Vocabulary and sounds, activity 2

January February March April May June July August September October November December

Lesson 25 Vocabulary and sounds, activity 6

The first of July, the twenty-third of September, the sixteenth of May, the second of April, the fifteenth of February, the thirtieth of October, the first of August

Lesson 26 Sounds and vocabulary, activity 1

/ɪ/: knit sing drink swim
/iː/: read eat leave see speak
/aɪ/: drive ride write like type

Lesson 26 Reading and listening, activity 2

Is this your guitar?
No, it isn't.
Can you play the guitar?
No, I can't. But I can play the piano.
Have you got a piano?
Yes, I have. It's in the living room.

Lesson 26 Reading and listening, activity 3

Do you like cooking?
No, I don't. I can't cook.
What do you eat?
I go to restaurants in the evening and I eat sandwiches for lunch. And you? Can you cook?
Yes, I can. I like cooking very much. I like Chinese food.
Oh, good. You can cook lunch!

Lesson 27 Listening, activity 2

Conversation 1

WAITER Good afternoon. Can I help you?

CUSTOMER Can I have a sandwich, please?

WAITER There's chicken and tomato, cheese or roast beef.

CUSTOMER Chicken and tomato, please.

WAITER Anything to drink?

CUSTOMER A bottle of mineral water.

WAITER Anything else?

CUSTOMER Can I have an ice cream and a cup of coffee, please?

WAITER Certainly. Thank you.

Conversation 2

WAITER Can I help you?

CUSTOMER Yes, please. Have you got any pizzas?

WAITER Yes. There's cheese and tomato or tuna.

CUSTOMER One cheese and tomato pizza, please. And have you got spaghetti bolognese?

WAITER Yes, we have.

CUSTOMER One spaghetti bolognese, please.

WAITER Anything to drink?

CUSTOMER A bottle of red wine and two glasses of water, please.

WAITER Anything else? A dessert or coffee?

CUSTOMER Two coffees, please.

Conversation 3

WAITER Can I help you?

CUSTOMER Can we have two tuna salads, please?

WAITER Two tuna salads. Anything to drink?

CUSTOMER A Coke and a glass of milk, please.

WAITER Anything else?

CUSTOMER Can we have some bread with the salads, please?

WAITER Certainly. A dessert or coffee?

CUSTOMER No coffee. Can we have two ice creams, please?

WAITER Yes. Thank you.

Lesson 28   Listening, activity 1

A Excuse me, please. Where's the chemist?
B It's in Church Street.
A And where's Church Street?
B Go along Castle Street. Turn right into Broad Street. Then turn right into Church Street. It's on your right.
A Thank you very much.

Lesson 28   Listening, activity 3

A Excuse me. Where's the market?
B It's in Broad Street.
A Where's Broad Street?
B Walk along Oxford Road for 100 metres. Turn left into Lion Street. Then turn right into Broad Street. The market is on your left.
A Thank you.

Lesson 29   Reading and listening, activity 3

JANET Hello. It's Janet. Is that you Paul?
PAUL Hello, Janet. How are you?
JANET Fine. How is everyone at home?
PAUL Very well. It's 2 o'clock here. Mum is working in the garden and Dad is walking in Hyde Park.
JANET Is Julia at home?
PAUL No, she isn't in London this weekend. She's staying with a friend in Edinburgh. They're sightseeing. What time is it in New York at the moment?
JANET It's nine o'clock in the morning here. People are getting up and starting to go out. It's a beautiful day.
PAUL What do most New Yorkers do on Sundays?
JANET Some people leave the city but many people go to Central Park. I can see the park from my flat. I can see people running and cycling and children playing basketball. In the afternoon a lot of families come to the park.
PAUL What are you doing?
JANET I'm lying on the sofa with a cup of coffee and I'm phoning all my friends in Britain! The family I work for are walking in the park at the moment! Say hello to Mum and Dad. Bye for now, Paul.
PAUL Bye, Janet.

Lesson 30   Listening, activity 1

MOTHER Are you getting up, Jim?
JIM Yes, I'm getting dressed. What time is it?
MOTHER Half past seven. Your father's waiting for you.
JIM Can I have some breakfast?
MOTHER I'm making coffee. And there are some cornflakes. But hurry up!
JIM OK. I'm coming.

Lesson 30   Listening, activity 3

DAD Hello, Laura. How are you?
LAURA Fine, thanks, Dad.
DAD What are you doing this evening?
LAURA I'm having dinner with friends.
DAD What are you cooking?
LAURA Chili con carne.
DAD Well, have a nice evening.
LAURA Thanks. See you at the weekend.
DAD Bye.

Lesson 31   Grammar and reading, activity 3

BILL Where are you going for your holiday?
JANE South Africa.
BILL Wonderful! When are you leaving?
JANE On Sunday. Our plane is at 3 pm.
BILL Who are you going with?
JANE A friend called Helen.
BILL How are you getting to the airport?
JANE We're going into London by bus, then we're taking a train to the airport.
BILL Are you staying in a hotel?
JANE Yes, we're staying in a hotel in Johannesburg for two nights. After that we're going to stay for a week with my uncle. He lives in Cape Town, by the sea.
BILL When are you coming home?
JANE On the 2nd of March. We're staying for two weeks.

Lesson 31   Listening and writing, activity 1

PHIL I'm going to Istanbul on Sunday.
LISA Great! Where are you leaving from?
PHIL I'm getting the plane from London, Heathrow.
LISA How are you getting to the airport?
PHIL I'm driving. I'm leaving my car at the airport. I'm only staying in Istanbul for four days.
LISA Who are you going with?
PHIL A friend from work. We're staying in a hotel in the city centre.
LISA What are you going to do in Istanbul.
PHIL We're going to see the Blue Mosque on Monday.
LISA Are you going on a boat trip on the Bosphorus?
PHIL No, we haven't got time. We're going to visit the Topkapi Palace on Wednesday morning.
LISA When are you coming home?
PHIL On Thursday evening.
LISA Well, enjoy your holiday!

Lesson 32   Reading and listening, activity 2

A Let's go out this evening.
B Yes, OK. What's on?
A There's a James Bond film.
B Where's it on?
A At the Palace.

Lesson 32   Reading and listening, activity 3

A Let's go out this Saturday.
B I'm sorry, but I'm busy. I'm going to stay with my parents.
A Well, how about going out this evening?
B Yes, OK. What's on?
A There's a T. S. Eliot play on at the Aldwych: *The Cocktail Party*.
B I'm sorry, but I don't like the theatre. How about going to the cinema?
A Yes, OK. What's on at the Odeon?
B There's a Sylvester Stallone film.
A I'm sorry, but I don't like Sylvester Stallone.
B Well, let's stay at home!

Lesson 33   Sounds, activity 1

1 It's a hot day.
2 We were at work.
3 She was unhappy.
4 We're bored.
5 Their friends were here.
6 They're thirsty.

Lesson 33   Sounds, activity 2

/æ/: camp happy hat pack
/eɪ/: sail play case plane
/ɔː/: awful always bored warm

Lesson 34   Listening, activity 1

Description 1
A What was your English teacher like when you were at school?
B His name was Mr Schmitt. He was tall and dark. He was quite good-looking.
A Was he a good teacher?
B Not really. His English was awful! But he was fun.

Description 2
A What was your English teacher at school like?
B Her name was Miss Chamoux. She was short and dark. She was about fifty when I was in her class at school.
A Was she a good teacher?
B Yes. She was very clever but she wasn't fun.

Description 3
A What was your English teacher at school like?
B His name was Mr James. He was short and fair with blue eyes.
A Was he a good teacher?
B His English was good but he wasn't very friendly. And he was always late for lessons. He wasn't my favourite teacher.

Lesson 38   Sounds and vocabulary, activity 4

1 Did you wait for a long time?
2 Did she help you?
3 Did they walk to the village?
4 Was the weather fine?
5 Did you stay at the hotel?
6 Did you take any photographs?
7 Did they follow the dog back to the village?

Lesson 38 Reading and listening, activity 4

Q Hello, Mrs Steele. Is this the dog that saved your daughter's life?

MRS STEELE Yes, that's right. This is Jet. He's the family dog and Candy's best friend.

Q Candy fell into the swimming pool. Is that right?

MRS STEELE Yes, she did. And she can't swim. She's only four.

Q Is the swimming pool in your garden?

MRS STEELE No. It was at a friend's house. We went to stay there one weekend.

Q Where were you when she fell into the pool?

MRS STEELE I was in the bathroom having a shower. The radio was on so I didn't hear Candy calling for help.

Q What did Jet do?

MRS STEELE He barked and jumped at the kitchen door until I opened it. Then he ran to the swimming pool and jumped in. I followed him and I pulled Candy out.

Q He's a very clever dog!

Lesson 39 Listening, activity 1

SUE Did you enjoy your trip to Paris, Cathy?

CATHY It was great! We had a wonderful time.

SUE How long did you go for?

CATHY Only three days but we visited lots of things.

SUE Did you go up the Eiffel Tower?

CATHY No, we didn't. The weather wasn't very good. It was foggy. But we went to the Louvre and saw the Vermeer exhibition. And climbed up the Sacre Coeur. We visited Notre Dame, too.

SUE How did you get to Paris?

CATHY By plane. We flew from Heathrow. It only took an hour.

SUE Did you go out in the evenings?

CATHY Yes, We found a really good restaurant in the Latin Quarter. And we went to the opera.

SUE Did you buy anything?

CATHY Yes. I bought some designer clothes. I spent quite a lot of money! And I bought some perfume for you on the plane. Here it is.

SUE Oh, thank you very much.

Lesson 40 Sounds, activity 2

/ɑː/: start car bark father can't aren't card
/eɪ/: take stay came game wait day play

Lesson 40 Sounds, activity 4

/ɒ/: stop got orange sorry office shop bottle
/əʊ/: close smoke moment hotel those

Answer Key

Lesson 1
VOCABULARY
2 1 ask   2 listen   3 read   4 write   5 say
3 listen   find   say   ask   read   repeat   write   match
4 please   your   what   name   and   hello   goodbye

FUNCTIONS
1 1 I'm Maria.
   2 Hello, Maria. I'm Frank.
   3 And what's your name?
   4 My name's John.
2 My name is Diana.
   I am Petra.

SOUNDS
2 1 syllable: name   what's   please   your   read   write
   2 syllables: hello   goodbye   listen   repeat

LISTENING AND WRITING
1 1 What's your name, please?
   2 I'm Petra.
   3 Hello, Petra.
   4 And what's your name?
   5 I'm Maria.
   6 Goodbye.
2 1 B   2 A
3 1 What's your   2 My name's, your name   3 My name's

WRITING
1 See the tapescript.

Lesson 2
VOCABULARY
2 1 student   2 waiter   3 engineer   4 actor   5 teacher   6 secretary   7 journalist   8 doctor.
3 1 what   2 waitress or actress   3 goodbye   4 waiter   5 job   6 your   7 hello   8 name   9 singer   10 journalist

GRAMMAR
1 1 What is your job?
   2 I am an engineer.
   3 My name is Sarah.
   4 What is your name?
   5 I am a secretary.
2 1 a   2 an   3 a   4 an   5 a   6 an
3 1 What is your name?
   2 What is your job?

SOUNDS
1 2 syllables: teacher   doctor   actress   singer
   3 syllables: engineer   journalist

LISTENING AND SPEAKING
1 Conversation 1: an engineer
   Conversation 2: I'm; your name?; I'm; your job; I'm a journalist.

Lesson 3
VOCABULARY
1 zero   one   two   three   four   five   six   seven   eight   nine   ten
2

3 please   goodbye   hello   thank you   four   eight   telephone

SOUNDS
2 six   three   nine   one   five   eight   ten   four   two   seven

GRAMMAR
1 1 Hello. How are you?
   2 Hello, John. How are you?
   3 Hello, Tony. I'm very well, thanks. How are you?
   4 I'm fine, thanks.
   5 I'm very well, thank you.
   6 What's your phone number?
2 1 I am fine   2 What is ...
   3 I am ...   4 My name is ...
   5 I am ...   6 What is ...
3 1 b   2 d   3 a   4 c

LISTENING AND SPEAKING
2 2 01295 906 725
   3 01692 594 829
   4 01580 731 426
4 Conversation 1: 01794 320 491
   Conversation 2: 01246 790 784

Lesson 4
VOCABULARY AND SOUNDS
3 1 name   2 what   3 please   4 hello   5 seven   6 are

GRAMMAR
1 1 ?   2 .   3 ?   4 .   5 ?   6 .
2 Nouns: name   number   job
   Verbs: is   are   am
3 *Example answers*
   1 What's your name?   2 Are you Henry?   3 How do you spell your name?   4 Are you Maria?   5 What's your job?   6 How are you?
4 1 My name's Janet.
   2 How do you spell that?
   3 I'm a teacher.
   4 What's your job?
   5 I'm very well, thank you.
   6 How are you?

READING AND LISTENING
1 1 d   2 b   3 a   4 c
2 See the tapescript.
3 See the tapescript.

Lesson 5

SOUNDS
1 Oo: England   Sweden
Thailand   Turkey
oO: Brazil   Japan
Ooo: Germany   India   Italy
Mexico

VOCABULARY AND SPEAKING
1 American   British   Japanese
Italian   French   Korean
Chinese   Russian   Swiss
2 1 He's from Turkey.   2 She's
from Italy.   3 I'm from England.
4 He's from Brazil.   5 You're
from the United States.
3 1 He's Japanese.   2 He's
Turkish.   3 She's American.
4 He's Russian.   5 She's French.

GRAMMAR
1 I am   you are   he is   she is
2 1 am   2 is   3 is   4 are
3 1 He's from Brazil.   2 She's
from Thailand.   3 I'm from … .
4 1 a   2 –   3 –   4 an

LISTENING AND SPEAKING
1 Hello. I'm Sammy
Hello, Sammy. My name's Janet.
Are you American, Janet?
No, I'm from Canada. And you?
Are you British?
Yes, I am. I'm from London.

Lesson 6

GRAMMAR
1 Verb: is   am   are
Pronoun: you   I   he   she   it
Adjective: Italian   married
fine   well   American
2 1 No, I'm not.   2 Yes, she is.
3 Yes, it is.   4 No, it isn't.
5 No, she isn't.   6 Yes, she is.
3 1 No, he isn't. He's American.
2 No, it isn't. It's a nationality.
3 No, he isn't. He's German.
4 No, I'm not. I'm a student.
5 No, it isn't. It's in the United
States.
4 *Example answers*
1 Are you Japanese?
2 Is he Italian?
3 Are you married?
4 Is she French?
5 Are you a teacher?

VOCABULARY AND SOUNDS
1 & 2   13 thirteen   20 twenty
12 twelve   5 five   15 fifteen
11 eleven   18 eighteen   9 nine
2 two   17 seventeen

READING AND LISTENING
1 1 teacher   2 student   3 taxi
driver   4 secretary
2 & 3 1 Bangkok Tokyo; Thai
Japanese
2 Marseilles Paris; American
British
3 is married isn't married;
Argentina Brazil
4 secretary doctor; is married
isn't married

WRITING
1 *Example answers*
Sean Williams is twenty-five.
He's British. He's from Brighton.
His address is 13, North Road,
Brighton. His phone number is
01237 691 423. He's a language
teacher.

Lesson 7

VOCABULARY AND SOUNDS
1 you two; your four; job from;
country number; phone no
5 35 thirty-five   18 eighteen
33 thirty-three   82 eighty-two
45 forty-five   1 one   62 sixty-
two   99 ninety-nine
100 a hundred   57 fifty-seven

GRAMMAR
1 I'm, I'm not, I am not
you're, you're not, you are not
he's, he's not, he is not
she's, she's not, she is not
it's, it's not, it is not
2 1 What's your job?
2 He isn't French.
3 Is your name Maria?
4 How old is she?
5 I'm a waiter.
6 You're from Brazil.
3 1 b   2 a   3 a   4 b   5 a
4 *Example answers*
1 How old are you?   2 How old
is he?   3 How old is she?
4 How old is it?
5 & 6
A How old is it?   It's three
months.
B How old is he?   He's nine.
C How old is she?   She's
seventeen.
D How old is she?   She's
twenty-three.
E How old is he?   He's eighty-
four.

LISTENING AND WRITING
1 *Example answers*
1 How old are you?
2 What's your nationality?
3 Where are you from?
4 What's your job?
5 Are you married?
2 1 Steffi Graf   2 Brad Pitt
3

	Brad Pitt	Steffi Graf
Name:	Brad Pitt	Steffi Graf
Age:	37	28
Nationality:	American	German
Town:	Los Angeles	Mannheim
Job:	actor	tennis player
Married:	no	no

Lesson 8

VOCABULARY
1
CAR   ACTOR   POLITICIAN
GROUP   TEAM   PRESENTER
SINGER
2 1 c   2 e   3 a   4 b   5 d
4 1 he   2 town   3 Brazil
4 married   5 his   6 favourite

GRAMMAR AND READING
1 I my; you your; he his; she her
2 1 her   2 his
3 1 What is his job?
2 His name is Steve.
3 Is she a secretary?
4 Newton is from Brazil.
5 Is Rio in Argentina?
6 His favourite town is
Marseilles.
4 1 an   2 –   3 an   4 –   5 a   6 a
5 1 What   2 Where   3 What
4 Where   5 Who
6 How/Where/Who   7 What
6 1 g   2 d   3 f   4 a   5 c
6 (How) b   7 e

LISTENING AND WRITING
1 A 3   B 2   C 1
2
Sam: New York   American
taxi driver   Phil Collins
Maria: Venice   Italian
journalist   Pavarotti
John: London   British
hairdresser   David Bowie

Lesson 9

GRAMMAR AND READING
1 I am   you are   he is   she is
it is   we are   you are
they are
2 1 is   2 are   3 am   4 are; are
5 Is   6 is   7 is   8 are
3 1 They   2 We   3 Is she
4 They   5 We
4 1 are; are; are; are; is; am
2 are; are; is; is; are
3 are; are; is; is; are
6 1 She's Canadian.   2 She's
twenty-one.   3 She's from
Toronto.   4 Lee and Joe.
5 No, they aren't.   6 Lee is a
doctor.   7 Steve is a teacher.
8 favourite cars   English teachers
neighbours   favourite singers
football teams   French
doctors

VOCABULARY AND LISTENING
1 girl   brother   man
friend   boy   neighbour
woman   sister
2 girls   brothers   men   friends
boys   neighbours   women
sisters
3 man: brother   man   boy
woman: girl   woman   sister
man or woman: friend
neighbour
4 1 B   2 A
5 Conversation 1
Amy: 19   nineteen
Sally: 19   nineteen
Sam: 22   twenty-two
Teddy: 15   fifteen
Janet: 29   twenty-nine
Conversation 2
John: 28   twenty-eight
Tom: 13   thirteen
Dick: 13   thirteen
Julia: 17   seventeen
Emma: 12   twelve

Lesson 10

VOCABULARY AND GRAMMAR
1 2 engineer   3 listen   4 Poland
5 ninety   6 video   7 boy
8 Thai
2 umbrellas   cassettes   clocks
sandwiches   watches   pens
numbers   buses   keys
3 *Example answers*
1 What are these/those?
2 What's this/that?   3 What are
these/those?   4 What's this/that?
4 & 5
1 What's this? It's a car.
2 What are these? They're
cassettes.
3 What are those? They're
burgers.
4 What are these? They're pens.
5 What's that? It's a clock.
6 What's this? It's an umbrella.
7 What's that? It's a television.
8 What are those? They're
glasses.
7 1 Who is he?   2 Who are they?
3 What is that?   4 What are
those?   5 Who is she?   6 What
is this?

SOUNDS
2 1 b   2 a   3 a   4 b

READING AND LISTENING
1 1 d   2 c   3 a   4 b

Lesson 11

VOCABULARY AND GRAMMAR
1 2 twenty-seven pounds sixty-
one pence
3 eighty-four pounds
4 eleven pounds forty-five
pence
5 a hundred and twenty-nine
pounds
6 thirty-three pounds ninety-
nine pence
7 two pounds thirty-five pence
8 eighty-nine pence
2 blue   white   black   green
red   yellow
3 1 personal stereos   2 sweaters
3 perfume   4 sunglasses
5 wallets   6 watches   7 pens
4 1 They're seventy-eight pounds.
2 It's thirty-nine pounds.
3 They're nineteen pounds.

LISTENING
1 £12.30; £9.99
2 & 3 See the tapescript.

GRAMMAR
Example answers
1 How much are these
sunglasses?
2 How much is this pen?
3 How much are these shoes?
4 How much is this jacket?
5 How much are these jeans?

Lesson 12

VOCABULARY
1 table 2 coat
3 keys 4 chair 5 bag
6 wallet 7 pen 8 postcard
9 photos 10 books 11 watch
12 radio

GRAMMAR
1 1 on 2 under 3 in
2 1 under 2 on 3 in 4 on 5 on
3 1 The books are on the table.
  2 The keys are under the chair.
  3 The watch is on the table.
  4 The coat is on the chair.
  5 The pen is in the bag.
4 1 C 2 D 3 A 4 B
5 1 It's Nelson Mandela.
  2 It's a sandwich.
  3 They are cassettes.
  4 They are students.
6 's possessive: brother's Annie's
  Sally's
  is: Where's name's What's
  Who's It's
7 2 This is Nathalie's coat. This is
  her coat.
  3 This is Reza's book. This is his
  book.
  4 This is Nathalie's watch. This is
  her watch.
  5 This is Reza's coat. This is his
  coat.
  6 This is Nathalie's book. This is
  her book.

LISTENING
2 Conversation 1: 2 5
  Conversation 2: 1 6
  Conversation 3: 3 4
3 1 d 2 f 3 a 4 c 5 b 6 e

Lesson 13

VOCABULARY
1 daughter sister wife son
  husband brother mother
2 man: son husband brother
  woman: daughter sister wife
  mother

GRAMMAR AND READING
1 I my; you your; he his; she her;
  it its; we our; they their
2 1 our 2 their 3 you 4 they
  5 are
5 1 My 2 my 3 We 4 My
  5 He 6 he 7 We/I 8 Our/My
  9 her 10 Our/My 11 She
  12 she 13 our/my 14 He
  15 He 16 his
6 1 Paul 2 Sally 3 Jennifer
  4 Tom 5 Charlie 6 Shirley
  7 Sue 8 Jim
  1 They are from Birmingham in
  England.
  2 Sue is their daughter.
  3 She's nineteen.
  4 Charlie is Sue and Paul's son.
  5 Charlie is twenty-seven.
  6 Shirley is a doctor.
  7 Yes, they've got a son.
  8 His name is Jim.

LISTENING
1 a 2 c 3 b

Lesson 14

VOCABULARY
1 Across: quiet clever fair
  white red tall black green
  Down: short fun pretty
  dark blue friendly

GRAMMAR
1 you've got you have got
  you haven't got
  he's/she's got he/she has got
  he/she hasn't got
  we've got we have got
  we haven't got
  they've got they have got
  they haven't got
2 1 have got 2 has got 3 has got
  4 haven't got 5 hasn't got
  6 have got
3 1 What's she like?
  2 She's got brown eyes.
  3 I haven't got any brothers and
  sisters.
  4 My brother's name is Bill.
  5 He's got fair hair.
  6 They haven't got any children.
4 1 b 2 a 3 b 4 a 5 b 6 a
5 1 d 2 c 3 e 4 a 5 b

READING
1 1 Joan 2 Fred 3 Graham
  4 Amy and Liza 5 Christine
2 1 Graham is Christine's brother.
  (Fred is Christine's father.)
  2 He's got black hair.
  3 Her sisters are fifteen. They are
  twins.
  4 Her mother's name is Joan.
  (Her sister's name is Amy.)
  5 Fred hasn't got any hair.
  (Graham has got dark hair.)

Lesson 15

VOCABULARY AND GRAMMAR
1 sit down turn off turn on
  turn up pick up come in
  take off put on put down
2 1 window 2 jacket/coat
  3 light/cassette player
  4 books/bag/CD/letter
  5 letter 6 jacket/coat
  7 books/bag/CD/letter/cassette
  player 8 CD
3 *Example answers*
  Close the door. Turn the
  television off. Open the
  window. Turn the light on.
  Take your coat off. Read this
  book.
4 1 Don't do activity 2. 2 Don't
  open the window. 3 Don't turn
  the cassette player off. 4 Don't
  read the instructions. 5 Don't
  close your books. 6 Don't read
  the letter.

READING AND LISTENING
1 A in a plane B in the classroom
  C at home
2 1 sit down 2 don't smoke
  3 close 4 open 5 don't do
  6 don't listen 7 put 8 come in
  9 take off 10 sit down

Lesson 16

VOCABULARY
1 Across: 2 school 4 work 5 flat
  7 coat 9 live 11 on
  Down: 1 go 2 shop 3 office
  6 off 8 to 10 in
2 1 we 2 read; close 3 office;
  house 4 our; their
  5 daughter; mother 6 sweater;
  skirt

GRAMMAR AND WRITING
1 1 in; in 2 to; in 3 in; in 4 in
  5 in; in 6 to
2 *Example answers*
  I work in an office. You go to
  school. We live in a house.
  You work in a shop.
3 doctor hospital; secretary office;
  shop assistant shop; teacher
  classroom; waiter restaurant
4 *Example answers*
  2 I live in Turkey. I'm a teacher
  and I work in a school.
  3 I live in Japan. I'm a secretary
  and I work in an office.
  4 I live in Mexico. I'm a shop
  assistant and I work in a shop.
  5 I live in France. I'm a waiter
  and I work in a restaurant.

Lesson 17

VOCABULARY
1 1 seven am 2 eight pm
  3 eleven am 4 three pm
  5 six pm 6 two pm
2 2 It's eight o'clock in the
  evening.
  3 It's eleven o'clock in the
  morning.
  4 It's three o'clock in the
  afternoon.
  5 It's six o'clock in the evening.
  6 It's two o'clock in the
  afternoon.

GRAMMAR
1
I: have work live was
you/we/they: have work live
  were
2 1 at; in 2 in 3 in 4 in; in
  5 at 6 at; in
3 I have breakfast at 8 o'clock.
  I have lunch in the afternoon.
  We work in an office.
  We work in a shop.
  They live in a flat. They live in a
  house in Florence.
4 *Example answers*
  2 What time is it?
  3 What's your job?
  4 What's your nationality?
  5 Have you got any brothers?
  6 How old are you?

READING
1 doctor, teacher
2 's, 'm, live, 'm, work, is, 's, have,
  have, have
3 Pierre
  breakfast: seven o'clock in the
  morning
  lunch: one o'clock in the
  afternoon
  dinner: eight o'clock in the
  evening
  Christine
  breakfast: eight o'clock in the
  morning
  lunch: one o'clock in the
  afternoon
  dinner: six o'clock in the evening
4 1 No, Pierre and Claire live in
  Toulouse.
  2 No, Pierre is a doctor in a
  hospital.
  3 No, they have breakfast at
  seven o'clock.
  4 No, they have dinner at eight
  o'clock in the evening.
5 1 Christine is English.
  2 No, he isn't. He's Polish.
  3 Christine is a secretary.
  4 Their son's name is Steve.
  5 Dinner is at six o'clock in the
  evening.

Lesson 18

VOCABULARY
1 Monday Tuesday
  Wednesday Thursday Friday
  Saturday Sunday
2 play: tennis football baseball
  music
  read: newspaper letter book
  postcard
  listen to: music radio CD

GRAMMAR
1 I work in a shop from Monday
  to Friday. In the evening I read
  or I watch television. On Friday I
  go to the cinema with friends.
  On Saturday morning I go
  shopping and in the afternoon I
  watch the sport on television or
  I play tennis with my son. On
  Sunday I have breakfast at
  eleven o'clock with my family
  and we go to see my parents in
  the afternoon. My favourite day
  is Sunday.
3 2 I don't go to the cinema ...
  3 I don't live ... 4 I don't work ...
  5 I don't live ... 6 I don't like ...
  7 I don't read ... 8 I don't see ...

SOUNDS
1 two syllables: today morning
  Wednesday breakfast
  birthday shopping
  three syllables: afternoon
  cinema radio Saturday
2 daughter Wednesday listen
  eight sandwich answer
  light

READING AND WRITING
1 2 It's nine o'clock on Saturday
  evening.
  3 It's seven o'clock on Monday
  morning.
  4 It's ten o'clock on Friday
  evening.
  5 It's three o'clock on Tuesday
  afternoon.
  6 It's eight o'clock on
  Wednesday evening.
2 2 They play football on Saturday
  evening.

3 They have breakfast at seven o'clock on Monday morning.
4 They go to the cinema on Friday evening.
5 They go to school on Tuesday afternoon.
6 They have dinner at eight o'clock on Wednesday evening.
3 is don't work have read listen go play see go

Lesson 19

VOCABULARY
1 1 meat 2 fish 3 chocolate 4 fruit 5 cake 6 beer 7 coffee 8 (orange) juice 9 wine
3 1 like 2 have 3 like 4 live 5 work 6 have 7 have 8 work

LISTENING AND SPEAKING
1 1 b 2 a
3 1 football 2 beer 3 chocolate 4 fish 5 burgers

GRAMMAR
1 1 Do you like tennis?
   2 They like sport very much.
   3 Do you work in an office?
   4 Do you live in a flat?
   5 I live in a house in London.
   6 Do you have lunch at home?

Lesson 20

VOCABULARY AND SOUNDS
1 2 12.45: a quarter to one
   3 6.30: half past six
   4 8.15: a quarter past eight
   5 3.45: a quarter to four
   6 9.30: half past nine
3 Across: start play read work go watch arrive leave
   Down: live have write do like be see finish
4 1 starts 2 go 3 write 4 has 5 play/watch 6 see

GRAMMAR
1
I: have go finish
you: have go finish
he/she: has goes finishes
we/they: have go finish
3 2 He leaves home at a quarter past eight in the morning.
   3 She starts work at nine o'clock in the morning.
   4 He finishes work at four o'clock in the afternoon.
   5 He arrives home at a quarter to five in the evening.
   6 She watches television in the evening.

READING
1 c1 a2 e3 h4 b5 g6 f7 d8
2 1 Jenny has breakfast with her husband.
   2 She arrives at work at a quarter to nine.
   3 She has lunch with a friend at half past twelve.
   4 She leaves the office at half past four.
   5 She watches television with her family in the evening.

LISTENING
1 half past seven a quarter past eight a quarter to nine nine o'clock half past twelve half past five six o'clock
3 1 has 2 arrives 3 has 4 goes 5 finishes

Lesson 21

VOCABULARY
1 Across: 2 train 3 bicycle Down: 1 boat 2 taxi 3 bus 4 car

GRAMMAR
1 1 Does; doesn't 2 Does; does 3 Do; don't 4 Do; do 5 Does; doesn't 6 Do; do
3 1 Does he go to work by car?
   2 Do you walk to school?
   3 Do they watch football on television?
   4 Does she go home by taxi?
   5 Does he have lunch at work?

SOUNDS
1 train day; time like; bus does; leave read; boat don't; car start

READING AND LISTENING
1 1 d 2 c 3 f 4 a 5 g 6 e 7 b
3 works lives works starts leaves finishes arrives has

Lesson 22

VOCABULARY AND LISTENING
1 1 bread 2 chicken 3 rice 4 vegetables 5 wine 6 water
2 2
3 1 lunch 2 breakfast 3 a cup of tea in bed 4 two cups of black coffee 5 egg; jam
4 1 5 6 8

GRAMMAR
1
I: don't eat don't drink
you: don't eat don't drink
he/she/it: doesn't eat doesn't drink
we/they: don't eat don't drink
2 1 I don't start work ...
   2 She doesn't eat ...
   3 They don't like ...
   4 He doesn't work ..
   5 She doesn't live ...
3 Example answers
   1 What do you have for breakfast?
   2 When do you drink beer?
   3 Where do you work?
   4 What do you do in the evening?
   5 When do you start work?
   6 What fruit do you like?

READING AND WRITING
1 Picture A
2 He watches television and has ... He doesn't eat ... so he has a big dinner. He has a salad then he eats ... He likes Mexican food ... He has chili .. He doesn't like beer, he usually drinks ... He doesn't eat fruit or drink coffee ...

Lesson 23

VOCABULARY
1 read: the newspaper a book
   stay: at home at a hotel in the sea on the beach in a flat in the mountains
   lie: on the beach
   swim: in the sea
   ski: in the mountains
   cook: dinner
   eat: in restaurants at home at a hotel on the beach in the mountains
2 1 go; lying; swimming 2 skiing; stay; cooking; eat 3 go; staying; read; watch

LISTENING
2 Mike likes: shopping for clothes; lying on the beach; listening to rock music; dancing
   Mike doesn't like: food shopping; walking; sightseeing; working; writing postcards
   Karen likes: shopping for clothes; working sightseeing; skiing
   Karen doesn't like: food shopping; watching television; writing postcards

GRAMMAR
1 1 likes; doesn't like; doesn't like; lies; listens; doesn't like; doesn't like; doesn't like; likes dancing
2 Example answers
   She likes shopping for clothes, working, sightseeing and skiing.
3 She doesn't like watching television, food shopping or writing postcards.
4 1 Who 2 What 3 Where/When 4 How/When 5 Where 6 What 7 When 8 Who
7 1 in 2 on 3 on; in 4 at 5 In; at 6 In 7 on 8 on

Lesson 24

VOCABULARY
1 kitchen garage garden toilet bedroom balcony bathroom living room

GRAMMAR
1 1 are 2 is 3 is 4 are 5 are 6 is
2 2 There isn't a shower ...
   3 There isn't a television ...
   4 There aren't any armchairs ...
   5 There aren't any cupboards ...
   6 There isn't a telephone ...

READING AND WRITING
2 1 B 2 A 3 C

LISTENING
1 Advertisement 2
2 1 Spanish 2 four 3 two beds 4 sofa bed 5 washing machine 6 telephone 7 table and four chairs 8 £250

Lesson 25

VOCABULARY AND SOUNDS
1 & 2 January February March April May June July August September October November December
3 second third fourth fifth sixth seventh eighth ninth tenth
5 the twenty-third of September the sixteenth of May the second of April the fifteenth of February the thirtieth of October the first of August

GRAMMAR
1 never sometimes often usually always
2 1 b 2 a 3 a 4 b 5 a

READING
1 usually usually always never sometimes often usually always usually sometimes always
2 Rachel invites friends to her house. She dances and has fun. Bob and Mary stay at home with their children. They go to bed at midnight.
   Joe goes to a restaurant. He dances in the fountain in Trafalgar Square.
3 1 sometimes 2 always 3 usually 4 always 5 usually

Lesson 26

SOUNDS AND VOCABULARY
1 /ɪ/: knit sing drink swim
   /iː/: read eat leave see speak
   /aɪ/: drive ride write like type
3 1 ride 2 drive 3 read 4 speak 5 write 6 swim
5 /æ/: 1 3 5
   /ə/: 2 4
6 play: the guitar, chess
   use: a computer
   ride: a bicycle
   speak: Japanese, Italian
   drive: a car
   read: letters
   cook: spaghetti
   write: letters
   understand: Japanese, Italian

READING AND LISTENING
1 1 b 2 c 3 a
3 1 c 2 e 3 a 4 f 5 b 6 d

WRITING
1 Example answers
   2 She can't cook. 3 They can't dance. 4 She can't swim. 5 He can't drive.

Lesson 27

VOCABULARY
1 A a glass B a cup C a bottle D piece
2 a piece of cake; a bottle/glass of juice; a piece of cheese; a piece of bread; a bottle/glass of wine;

a cup of coffee; a piece of pizza;
a bottle/glass of milk

SOUNDS
1 1 bread 2 piece 3 fruit
   4 bottle 5 garlic

LISTENING
1 Table A: a sandwich, a bottle of
   mineral water
   Table B: salad, a coke and a
   glass of milk, bread
   Table C: a pizza, spaghetti,
   wine, water
2 Conversation 1: Table A
   Conversation 2: Table C
   Conversation 3: Table B
3 See answers to activity 1.

READING AND WRITING
1 *Example answers*
   Can I have a sandwich, please?
   A chicken sandwich, please.
   Can I have a cup of coffee,
   please?
   Have you got any desserts?
   Cheesecake, please.

Lesson 28
VOCABULARY
1 Across: 1 chemist 5 bank
   6 park 7 bookshop
   Down: 2 market 3 station
   4 baker 6 pub
2 1 north 2 west 3 east
   4 south

READING AND FUNCTIONS
1 1 It's in Castle Street.
   2 It's in Castle Street.
   3 It's in the car park.
   4 It's in Church Street.
2 in Where's along turn on
   in Where's along on
3 1 bookshop 2 cinema 3 bank
   4 post office 5 toilet 6 chemist

LISTENING
1 chemist; along; right; right; right
3 Where's the **market**? **Walk**
   along Oxford Road. Turn **left**
   into Lion Street. Then turn **right**
   into Broad Street. The market is
   on your left.

SOUNDS
3 Bramley
4 Start your tour of Bramley at the
   car park. Go along Oak Road.
   Turn right into Green Street. The
   bank is on your right and the
   market is straight ahead. Turn
   left into Elm Street. The post
   office is on the left.

Lesson 29
VOCABULARY
1 shopping running sitting
   stopping getting swimming
   knitting smoking writing
   dancing leaving having
   driving typing
2 2 He's swimming.
   3 They're dancing.
   4 He's running. 5 She's driving.
   6 She's knitting.

GRAMMAR
1 1 are 2 is 3 is 4 are 5 is
2 1 buying 2 playing 3 having
   4 standing 5 dancing 6 leaving
3 *Example answers*
   1 She's working.
   2 He's reading.
   3 They are talking.
   4 He's driving to work.
   5 He's eating pizza.

READING AND LISTENING
1 1 Janet is in New York.
   2 Paul is at home in London.
2 1 d 2 b 3 a 4 e 5 c
4 1 It's nine o'clock in the
     morning.
   2 It's two o'clock.
   3 His mother is working in the
     garden and his father is walking
     in Hyde Park.
   4 She's in Edinburgh.
   5 They are running and cycling.
   6 She's lying on the sofa with a
     cup of coffee. She's telephoning
     her friends in Britain.

Lesson 30
VOCABULARY
1 Across: wear stay learn
   wait talk speak be get
   Down: buy draw lie use
   sit run teach do go eat
   walk cook
2 1 waiting 2 learning/teaching
   3 cooking/eating 4 staying
   5 wearing 6 lying
3 1 green; red 2 at; to 3 jeans;
   jacket 4 library; baker
   5 wine; water 6 September;
   March
   7 Tuesday; Wednesday 8 first;
   second 9 nice; clever
   10 daughter; brother

SOUNDS
1 1 wear 2 watch 3 start 4 sit

GRAMMAR
1 1 What are you doing?
   2 We are waiting for a taxi.
   3 Is she making coffee?
   4 They are not watching
     television.
   5 He is not coming to school.
2 1 No, he isn't making tea, he's
     making coffee.
   2 No, they aren't waiting for a
     taxi, they're waiting for a bus.
   3 No, she isn't getting dressed,
     she's having a shower.
   4 No, we aren't going to the
     cinema, we're going to the
     theatre.
   5 No, he isn't talking to his
     brother, he's talking to a friend.
3 1 Is she having a party?
   2 Are they wearing jeans?
   3 Are we going to the cinema?
   4 Are you waiting for your
     brother?
   5 Is he staying at the hotel?

LISTENING
1 1 I'm getting dressed
   2 is waiting 3 'm making

4 'm coming
3 & 4 at midday: this evening
   having lunch with friends:
   having dinner with friends
   Pasta and salad: chili con carne
   enjoy yourself: have a nice
   evening
   tomorrow: at the weekend

Lesson 31
VOCABULARY
1 nouns: week case
   plane boat beach tent
   mountain city sea hour
   visa airport sightseeing
   verbs: wear sail meet stay
   spend pack get travel
2 1 week 2 case 3 staying
   4 sightseeing 5 plane; meeting
   6 tent 7 spend 8 beach; sea

GRAMMAR AND READING
1 1 Where 2 Who 3 Are; are
   4 When 5 How 6 Who
   7 How/When 8 When/How
2 2 When are you leaving?
   3 Who are you going with?
   4 How are you getting to the
     airport? 5 Are you staying in a
     hotel? 6 When are you coming
     home?
4 1 Where is she going for her
     holiday? 2 When is she leaving?
   3 Who is she going with?
   4 How is she getting to the
     airport? 5 Is she staying in a
     hotel? 6 When is she coming
     home?
5 2 She's leaving on Sunday.
   3 She's going with a friend.
   4 She's taking a train to the
     airport. 5 Yes, she's staying in a
     hotel. 6 She's coming home on
     the 2nd of March.

LISTENING AND WRITING
1 1 4 5 6 8 9
3 I'm sitting; I'm having; we're
   going; We're staying; we're
   taking; we're going; I'm coming;
   I'm driving
4 future plans: we're going to a
   club; we're taking a taxi; we're
   going shopping; I'm coming
   home; I'm driving
   at the moment: I'm sitting; I'm
   having; We're staying

Lesson 32
VOCABULARY AND READING
1 film cinema; jazz music club;
   play theatre; concert concert
   hall; exhibition gallery
2 1 film 2 concert 3 play
   4 art exhibition 5 jazz concert
3 1 Concorde 2 The English
   Patient; 16th May 3 Komedia
   4 Royal Pavilion Monday 12th
   May 5 Grange Gallery 10 May
   to 15 June

FUNCTIONS
1 1 go 2 going 3 going 4 go
   5 go 6 going
3 *Example answers*

How about; What's on? I don't
like James Bond.; let's; on
4 1 on 2 to 3 at 4 at 5 on

READING AND LISTENING
1 Let's go out this evening
   Yes, OK. What's on?
   There's a James Bond film.
   Where's it on?
   At the Palace.
3 1 this Saturday 2 busy
   3 evening 4 play 5 theatre
   6 cinema 7 film

Lesson 33
VOCABULARY
1 awful warm tired bored
   nice happy cold friendly
2 positive: happy nice clever
   warm
   negative: bored tired
   unhappy ill

SOUNDS
1 1 b 2 a 3 b 4 a 5 b 6 b
3 /æ/: camp happy hat pack
   /eɪ/: sail play case plane
   /ɔː/: awful always bored
   warm

GRAMMAR
1 1 I was; you were; he/she/it
   was; we/they were
2 1 were 2 was 3 was 4 was
   5 were 6 were 7 were 8 was
3 present: today this year
   this week
   past: yesterday last week
   the last time last year
4 1 d 2 e 3 f 4 b 5 a 6 c

READING
1 1 b 2 c 3 a
2 1 woman 2 man 3 woman
3 1 a warm b wonderful c good
   2 a busy b closed c awful
   3 a busy b awful

Lesson 34
VOCABULARY
1 murder hungry Miss
   butler wine murderer
   colonel Mrs scream
   detective professor dead
   Lady
2 1 awful 2 thirsty 3 everything
   4 alone 5 knife 6 anyone
   7 hungry 8 something

GRAMMAR
1 1 Were 2 Was 3 Were 4 Was
   5 Was 6 Were
2 1 f 2 d 3 a 4 c 5 b 6 e
3 *Example answers*
   1 Was the food good?
   2 Were they nice/friendly?
   3 Was there anything on the
     table? 4 Was he in the kitchen?
   5 Was there any wine to drink?
   6 Was she alone?
4 1 us 2 her 3 them 4 it
5 1 Yes, they were. No, they
     weren't. 2 Yes, I am. No, I'm
     not. 3 Yes, he does. No, he
     doesn't. 4 Yes, it is. No, it isn't.
   5 Yes, there was. No, there wasn't.

6 Yes, he is. No, he isn't.
7 Yes, they are. No, they aren't.
8 Yes, he was. No, he wasn't.

LISTENING
1 Description 1: B Description
2: A Description 3: C
2 1 3 5 6 7 9

Lesson 35
VOCABULARY
1 personal stereo fax machine
vacuum cleaner washing
machine

SOUNDS
3 <u>c</u>offee to<u>b</u>a<u>cc</u>o po<u>t</u>a<u>t</u>oes
<u>s</u>and<u>w</u>ich <u>c</u>ameras ma<u>ch</u>ine
engine <u>new</u>spaper
<u>g</u>unpowder re<u>cor</u>der

GRAMMAR
1 1 had 2 have 3 have 4 had
5 have 6 have 7 had; had
8 have
2 1 I did not have a television.
2 We had a dishwasher when I
was a child.
3 There was a computer at my
school.
4 Did you have a good holiday?
5 I had a sandwich for lunch.
4 *Example answers*
1 Did you have a car when you
were a child?
2 Did you have a radio?
3 Did you have a television?
4 Did you have a dishwasher?
5 Were there computers in your
school?

READING AND WRITING
1 1 c 2 g 3 a 4 f 5 b
2 *Example answers*
1 Did you have a television
when you were a child?
2 Have you got a fax machine?

Lesson 36
VOCABULARY
1 1 this 2 last 3 last 4 last
5 this 6 this
2 3 4 6 8

READING
1 had travelled travelled
hired visited stayed
visited liked decided
camped walked cooked
finished stayed had
travelled was
2 Venice: four nights Florence:
three nights The Abruzzes
mountains: two nights
Rome: five nights.
3 1 the Abruzzes mountains
2 Milan 3 Florence 4 Venice
5 the Abruzzes mountains
6 Rome

GRAMMAR
1 walked watched cooked
stayed started travelled
played visited had lived
was/were finished worked
2 1 started; was 2 lived; worked

3 was; played 4 started; finished
5 was/stayed 6 was; watched
4 1 in 2 from; to 3 at; in 4 at
5 on 6 at

Lesson 37
SOUNDS
1 1 finished 2 worked 3 arrived
4 visited
2 2 5

GRAMMAR
1 1 She started work at ten
yesterday.
2 He didn't want to live in
London.
3 Picasso was born in 1881 in
Malaga./Picasso was born in
Malaga in 1881.
4 We lived in Bangkok for three
years.
5 They didn't watch television
last night.
6 He started to paint when he
was ten.
2 1 don't; don't 2 didn't 3
doesn't 4 didn't 5 don't
6 didn't
3 1 We didn't live .. 2 She didn't
work ... 3 He didn't study ...
4 Picasso didn't paint ...
5 He didn't die ... 6 He didn't
return ...

READING
1 1 Marie Curie 2 Albert Einstein
3 Salvador Dali
2 1 was 2 received 3 studied
4 changed 5 married 6 died
3 1 She didn't work with her
brother. She worked with her
husband.
2 He didn't study in Berne. He
studied in Zürich.
3 He didn't receive the Nobel
prize in 1911. He received it in
1921.
4 Dali didn't live in Paris until
1927. He lived in Paris until
1938.
5 Dali didn't live in Paris until he
died. He returned to Spain.

Lesson 38
SOUNDS AND VOCABULARY
1 <u>recognise</u> ap<u>pear</u> <u>happen</u> <u>realise</u>
disap<u>pear</u> <u>follow</u> de<u>cide</u> re<u>turn</u>
3 1 e 2 f 3 g 4 a 5 d 6 c
7 b
5 1 walk 2 call 3 last 4 cold
5 still
7 1 dark 2 call 3 stay/wait
4 lots 5 find

GRAMMAR
1 1 did 2 did 3 does 4 did
5 do 6 did

READING AND LISTENING
2 Picture 3
3 was saved was was fell
started barked opened ran
4 a swimming pool in the Steele
family's garden
in the kitchen
Jet barked at the kitchen door

5 B ...The children were very
frightened and they shouted for
help. Their dog, Leo, saved their
lives. He jumped in front of
them and barked at the snake
until it disappeared behind a
tree. The snake bit the dog and
he died.
C ... His owner, Mrs Dickens,
closed the door and started the
machine. He stayed ten minutes
in the machine before Mrs
Dickens noticed him through
the glass door. She stopped the
machine and pulled a very clean
cat out. He didn't sleep in the
washing machine again!

Lesson 39
VOCABULARY
1 Across: 1 passport 6 timetable
8 credit card
Down: 2 posters 3 ticket
4 receipt 5 brochure 7 bill
2 pay bill spend money
look at timetable/photograph
take photograph stay hotel
have dinner

GRAMMAR
1 1 Where 2 Where/How long
3 What 4 Who 5 How/When
6 How much
3 bought flew left saw
gave came found got
did spent went took
4 1 bought 2 got 3 took
4 flew 5 saw 6 went

LISTENING
1 1 b 2 f 3 d 4 a 5 c 6 e
2 1 4 5
3 2 She stayed there for three
days.
3 The weather wasn't very good.
It was foggy.
6 She bought some designer
clothes and some perfume.

Lesson 40
VOCABULARY
1 peaceful dark beautiful
foggy dirty clever
thirsty quiet wonderful
hungry
2 1 railway station 2 dream
3 flowers 4 bird 5 village
6 bill 7 credit card 8 gallery
3 1 thirsty 2 foggy 3 dirty
4 quiet 5 wonderful

GRAMMAR
1 present simple: 3 7 8
present continuous: 1 5 10
past simple: 2 4 6 9
2 spent   had   arrived
  left   wrote   gave
  wore   heard   was
  knew   brought   flew
  came   drank   met
3 bought   took   went
  made   ran   got
  was/were   saw   said
  happened   thought   sold
  ate   did   found

4 1 flew 2 bought 3 arrive/get
4 went/flew 5 saw 6 took
7 had 8 wrote 9 met/saw
10 gave
6 1 c 2 d 3 g 4 h 5 b 6 e
7 a 8 f
7 *Example answers*
B They are waiting for a bus.
C She is taking a photograph.
D It is barking.
E He is lying on the beach.
F She is writing a letter

SOUNDS
1 /ɑː/: start car   bark
father can't aren't
card
/eɪ/: take stay came
game wait day play
3 /ɒ/: stop got orange
sorry office shop bottle
/əʊ/: close smoke moment
hotel those
5 <u>passenger</u> <u>photograph</u>
exhi<u>bition</u> <u>country</u> disap<u>pear</u>
<u>platform</u> un<u>happy</u>
Sep<u>tember</u> after<u>noon</u>

Wordlist

The first number after each word shows the lesson in which the word first appears in the vocabulary box. The numbers in *italics* show the later lessons in which the word appears again

a quarter past /ə kɔːtə pɑːst/ 20
a quarter to /ə kɔːtə tuː/ 20
actor /æktə/ 2
actress /æktrəs/ 2
address /ədres/ 6
afternoon /ɑːftənuːn/ 17
age /eɪdʒ/ 6
am /æm/ 17
America /əmerɪkə/ 21
American /əmerɪkən/ 5
apple /æpəl/ 22
apple pie / æpəl paɪ/ 27
April /eɪprəl/ 25
armchair /ɑːmtʃeə/ 24
arrive /əraɪv/ 20
Asia /eɪʃə/ 21
August /ɔːgəst/ 25
awful /ɔːfʊl/ 33

back /bæk/ 24
bag /bæg/ 10, 12, 15
baker /beɪkə/ 28
bank /bæŋk/ 28
bark /bɑːk/ 38
baseball /beɪsbɔːl/ 19
basket ball /bɑːskɪtbɔːl/ 19
bathroom /bɑːθruːm/ 24
be born /bɪ bɔːn/ 37
beach /biːtʃ/ 31
bed /bed/ 24
bedroom /bedruːm/ 24
beef /biːf/ 22
beer /bɪə/ 22
bicycle /baɪsɪkəl/ 21, 26, 35
bill /bɪl/ 39
bird /bɜːd/ 38
black /blæk/ 11, 14
blue /bluː/ 11, 14
boat /bəʊt/ 21
book /bʊk/ 15
books /bʊks/ 10
bookshop /bʊkʃɒp/ 28
bored /bɔːd/ 33
bottle /bɒtəl/ 27
boy /bɔɪ/ 9

Brazil /brəzɪl/ 5
Brazilian /brəzɪlɪən/ 5
bread /bred/ 22, 27
Britain /brɪtən/ 5
British /brɪtɪʃ/ 5
brochure /brəʊʃʊə/ 39
brother /brʌðə/ 9
brothers /brʌðəž/ 13
brown /braʊn/ 14
burger /bɜːgə/ 10
bus /bʌs/ 10, 21
buy /baɪ/ 29

cake /keɪk/ 27
camp /kæmp/ 31
car /kɑː/ 8, 21, 35
car park /kɑː pɑːk/ 28
cases /keɪsɪz/ 31
cassette player /kəset pleɪə/ 15
cassettes /kəsets/ 10
cat /kæt/ 38
chair /tʃeə/ 12
cheese /tʃiːz/ 27
chemist /kemɪst/ 28
chicken /tʃɪkɪn/ 22
children /tʃɪldrən/ 13
cinema /sɪnəmə/ 10, 28, 32
city /sɪtiː/ 31
climb /klaɪm/ 38
clock /klɒk/ 10
club /klʌb/ 32
coat /kəʊt/ 15
coat pocket /kəʊt pɒkɪt /12
coffee /kɒfiː/ 10, 22, 27
cold /kəʊld/ 33
computer /kəmpjuːtə/ 26, 35
concert /kɒnsət/ 32
concert hall /kɒnsət hɔːl /32
cook /kʊk/ 26
cooker /kʊkə/ 24
country /kʌntriː/ 5
cup /kʌp/ 27
cupboard /kʌbəd/ 24

dance /dɑːns/ 26, 29
dancing /dɑːnsɪŋ/ 23
dark /dɑːk/ 14, 38
daughters /dɔːtəz/ 13
December /dɪsembə/ 25
die /daɪ/ 37
dining room / daɪnɪŋ ruːm/ 24

disappear /dɪsəpɪə/ 38
dishwasher /dɪʃwɒʃə/ 35
doctor /dɒktə/ 2
dog /dɒg/ 38
door /dɔː/ 15
downstairs /daʊnstəz/ 24
draw /drɔː/ 26
drink /drɪŋk/ 22, 29
drive /draɪv/ 26, 29, 29

eating in restaurants /iːtɪŋ ɪn restrɒnts/ 23
eight /eɪt/ 3
eighteen /eɪtiːn/ 6
eighth /eɪθ/ 25
eighty /eɪtiː/ 7
eleven /ɪlevən/ 6
eleventh /ɪlevənθ/ 25
engineer /endʒɪnɪə/ 2
English /ɪŋglɪʃ/ 26
Europe /jʊərəp/ 21
evening /iːvnɪŋ/ 17
exhibition /eksɪbɪʃən/ 32
eyes /aɪs/ 14

fair /feə/ 14
father /fɑːðə/ 13
favourite /feɪvrət/ 8
fax machine /fæks məʃiːn/ 35
February /febjʊəriː/ 25
fifteen /fɪftiːn/ 6
fifth /fɪθ/ 25
fifty /fɪftiː/ 7
film /fɪlm/ 32
fine /faɪn/ 33
finish /fɪnɪʃ/ 20, 37
first /fɜːst/ 25
five /faɪv/ 3
flat /flæt/ 16
foggy /fɒgiː/ 38
food /fuːd/ 22
football /fʊtbɔːl/ 10, 19, 26
football team /fʊtbɔːl tiːm/ 8
forty /fɔːtiː/ 7
four /fɔː/ 3
fourteen /fɔːtiːn/ 6
fourth /fɔːθ/ 25
French /frentʃ/ 26
Friday /fraɪdeɪ/ 18
friend /frend/ 9
friendly /frendliː/ 14
front /frʌnt/ 24
fruit /fruːt/ 22

gallery /ɡæləri:/ 32
garden /ɡɑːdən/ 24
get /ɡet/ 31
get dressed /ɡet drest/ 29
get up /ɡet ʌp/ 29
girl /ɡɜːl/ 9
glass /ɡlɑːs/ 27
glasses /ɡlɑːsɪz/ 10, 12
go /ɡəʊ/ 16
go for a walk /ɡəʊ fɔː a wɔːk/ 18
go home /ɡəʊ həʊm/ 20
go shopping /ɡəʊ ʃɒpɪŋ/ 18
go straight ahead /ɡəʊ streɪt əhed/ 28
go to the cinema /ɡəʊ tuː ðə sɪnəmə/ 18
good-looking /ɡʊdlʊkɪŋ/ 14
goodbye /ɡʊdbaɪ/ 2
green /ɡriːn/ 11, 14
group /ɡruːp/ 8
guitar /ɡɪtɑː/ 26
gymnastics /dʒɪmnæstɪks/ 19
hair /heə/ 14
half past /hɑːf pɑːst/ 20
hall /hɔːl/ 24
happy /hæpi:/ 33
hat /hæt/ 31
have /hæv/ 29, 30
have breakfast /hæv brekfəst/ 17
have dinner /hæv dɪnə/ 17
have lunch /hæv lʌntʃ/ 17
hello /heləʊ/ 1
hot /hɒt/ 33
house /haʊs/ 16
hungry /hʌngri:/ 34
husband /hʌzbənd/ 13

individual sport /ɪndɪvɪdjʊəl spɔːt/ 19
Italian /ɪtælɪən/ 5, 26
Italy /ɪtəli:/ 5

jacket /dʒækɪt/ 11
January /dʒænjʊəri:/ 25
Japan /dʒəpæn/ 5
Japanese /dʒæpəniːz/ 5
jeans /dʒiːnz/ 11
job /dɒb/ 2, 6
journalist /dʒɜːnəlɪst/ 2
juice /dʒuːs/ 22
July /dʒuːlaɪ/ 25
June /dʒuːn/ 25

keys /kiːz/ 10, 12
kitchen /kɪtʃɪn/ 24
lamb /læm/ 22
large /lɑːdʒ/ 24
last month /lɑːst mʌnθ/ 36
last week /lɑːst wiːk/ 36

last year /lɑːst jɪə/ 36
leave /liːv/ 20
lemon /lemən/ 22
lettuce /letɪs/ 27
library /laɪbri:/ 28
lie /laɪ/ 29
light /laɪt/ 15
like /laɪk/ 19
listen /lɪsən/ 30
live /lɪv/ 16, 37
living room /lɪvɪŋ ruːm/ 24
lying on the beach /laɪɪŋ ɒn ðə biːtʃ/ 23

make /meɪk/ 30
man /mæn/ 9
March /mɑːtʃ/ 25
market /mɑːkɪt/ 28
married /mærɪd/ 6
May /meɪ/ 25
meat /miːt/ 22
meet /miːt/ 31
milk /mɪlk/ 22, 27
Monday /mʌndeɪ/ 18
morning /mɔːnɪŋ/ 17
mother /mʌðə/ 13
mountains /maʊntɪns/ 31
music /mjuːsɪk/ 32

name /neɪm/ 6
nationality /næʃənælɪtɪː/ 5, 6
neighbour /neɪbə/ 9
nice /naɪs/ 14
nine /naɪn/ 3
nineteen /naɪntiːn/ 6
ninety /naɪnti:/ 7
ninth /naɪnθ/ 25
November /nəʊvembə/ 25

o'clock /əklɒk/ 17
October /ɒktəʊbə/ 25
office /ɒfɪs/ 16
one /wʌn/ 3
one hundred /wʌn hʌndrəd/ 7
orange /ɒrɪndʒ/ 22, 27
outback /aʊtbæk/ 31

pack /pæk/ 31
paint /peɪnt/ 37
painting /peɪntɪŋ/ 37
passenger /pæsɪndʒə/ 40
pen /pen/ 10, 15
pence /pens/ 11
personal stereo /pɜːsənəl sterɪəʊ/ 12, 35
piano /pjænəʊ/ 26
piece /piːs/ 27
pizza /piːtzə/ 10

plane /pleɪn/ 31
platform /plætfɔːm/ 40
play /pleɪ/ 26, 29, 32
pm /piː em/ 17
politician /pɒlɪtɪʃən/ 8
post office /pəʊst ɒfɪs/ 28
potato /pəteɪtəʊ/ 22
pound /paʊnd/ 11
pretty /prɪti:/ 14
pub /pʌb/ 28

quiet /kwaɪət/ 14
quite /kwaɪt/ 14

radio /reɪdiːəʊ/ 35
railway /reɪlweɪ/ 40
read /riːd/ 29
reading /riːdɪŋ/ 23
receipts /rɪsiːts/ 39
red /red/ 11, 14
restaurant /restrɒnt/ 28
rice /raɪs/ 22
ride /raɪd/ 26
run /rʌn/ 29
running /rʌnɪŋ/ 19
Russia /rʌʃə/ 5
Russian /rʌʃən/ 5

sailing /seɪlɪŋ/ 19
sandwich /sænwɪdʒ/ 10
Saturday /sætədeɪ/ 18
school /skuːl/ 16
sculpture /skʌlptʃə/ 37
sea /siː/ 31
second /sekənd/ 25
secretary /sekrəteri:/ 2
see /siː/ 29
see friends /siː frends/ 18
September /septembə/ 25
seven /sevən/ 3
seventeen /seventiːn/ 6
seventh /sevənθ/ 25
seventy /seventi:/ 7
shirt /ʃɜːt/ 11
shoes /ʃuːs/ 11
shop /ʃɒp/ 16, 29
short /ʃɔːt/ 14
shower /ʃaʊwə/ 24
sightseeing /saɪtsiːɪŋ/ 23
sing /sɪŋ/ 26
singer /sɪŋə/ 2
sister /sɪstə/ 9
sisters /sɪstəž/ 13
sit /sɪt/ 29
sitting in the sun /sɪtɪŋ ɪn ðə sʌn/ 23
six /sɪks/ 3

sixteen /sɪksti:n/ 6
sixth /sɪkθ/ 25
sixty /sɪksti:/ 7
skiing /ski:ɪŋ/ 19, 23
skirt /skɜ:t/ 11
small /smɔ:l/ 24
sofa /səʊfə/ 24
sons /sʌnz/ 13
speak /spi:k/ 26
spend /spend/ 31
stand /stænd/ 29
start /stɑ:t/ 20, 37
station /steɪʃən/ 28
staying in hotels /steɪjɪŋ ɪn həʊtels/ 23
stop /stɒp/ 29
student /stu:dənt/ 2
study /stʌdi:/ 37
Sunday /sʌndeɪ/ 18
sweater /swetə/ 11
swim /swɪm/ 26
swimming /swɪmɪŋ/ 19, 23

table /teɪbəl/ 12
table tennis /teɪbəl tenɪs/ 19
talk /tɔ:k/ 30
tall /tɔ:l/ 14
taxi /tæksi:/ 10, 21
tea /ti:/ 22
teacher /ti:tʃə/ 2
team sport / ti:m spɔ:t/ 19
telephone /teləfəʊn/ 10, 35
telephone number /teləfəʊn nʌmbə/ 3
television /teləvɪʒən/ 10, 35
ten /ten/ 3
tennis /tenɪs/ 10, 19, 26
tenth /tenθ/ 25
Thai /taɪ/ 5
Thailand /taɪlənd/ 5
the United States of America /ðə ju:naɪtɪd
    steɪts ɒv əmerɪkə/ 5
theatre /θɪətə/ 10, 32
third /θɜ:d/ 25
thirsty /θɜ:sti:/ 34
thirteen /θɜ:ti:n/ 6
thirty /θɜ:ti:/ 7
thirty-one /θɜ:ti: wʌn/ 7
this month /ðɪs mʌnθ/ 36
this week /ðɪs wi:k/ 36
this year /ðɪs jɪə/ 36
three /θri:/ 3
Thursday /θɜ:zdeɪ/ 18
ticket office /tɪkɪt ɒfɪs/ 40
tickets /tɪkɪts/ 31, 39
tired /taɪəd/ 33
today /tədeɪ/ 36
tomato /təmɑ:təʊ/ 22, 27

train /treɪn/ 21
Tuesday /tju:zdeɪ/ 18
Turkey /tɜ:ki:/ 5
Turkish /tɜ:kɪʃ/ 5
turn left /tɜ:n left/ 28
turn right /tɜ:n raɪt/ 28
TV presenter /ti: vi: prəzentə/ 8
TV programme /ti: vi: prəʊgræm/ 8
twelfth /twelθ/ 25
twelve /twelv/ 6
twenty /twenti:/ 6
twenty- eight /twenti: eɪt/ 7
twenty-five /twenti: faɪv/ 7
twenty-four /twenti: fɔ:/ 7
twenty-nine /twenti: naɪn/ 7
twenty-one /twenti: wʌn/ 7
twenty-seven /twenti: sevən/ 7
twenty-six /twenti: sɪks/ 7
twenty-three /twenti: θri:/ 7
twenty-two /twenti: tu:/ 7
twin /twɪn/ 9
two /tu:/ 3
type /taɪp/ 26

umbrella /ʌmbrelə/ 10
understand /ʌndəstænd/ 26
unhappy /ʌnhæpi:/ 33
upstairs /ʌpsteəz/ 24
use /ju:z/ 26

vacuum cleaner /vækju:m kli:nə/ 35
vegetable /vedʒtəbəl/ 22
very /veri:/ 14
video /vɪdɪəʊ/ 10
video recorder /vɪdɪəʊ rekɔ:də/ 35
village /vɪlɪdʒ/ 38
visit /vɪzɪt/ 20
volleyball /vɒlɪbɔ:l/ 19

wait /weɪt/ 30
waiter /weɪtə/ 2
waiting room /weɪtɪŋ ru:m/ 40
walk /wɔ:k/ 21, 29
walking /wɔ:kɪŋ/ 23
wallet /wɒlɪt/ 10, 12
warm /wɔ:m/ 33
wash /wɒʃ/ 29
watch /wɒtʃ/ 10, 12, 29
watch television /wɒtʃ teləvɪʒən/ 18
water /wɔ:tə/ 22, 27
wear /weə/ 31
weather /weðə/ 38
Wednesday /wenzdeɪ/ 18
white /waɪt/ 11
wife /waɪf/ 13
window /wɪndəʊ/ 15

wine /waɪn/ 22
woman /wʊmən/ 9
work /wɜ:k/ 16, 37
write letters /raɪt letəz/ 18
writing postcards /raɪtɪŋ pəʊstkɑ:dz/ 23

yesterday /jestədeɪ/ 36
yoghurt /jɒgət/ 22

zero /zɪərəʊ/ 3

94

Wordbank

Use the categories below to help you organise new vocabulary. Try and write each new word in at least two different categories. You may also like to write down words which often go with the new vocabulary items.

character	clothes	countries and nationalities
crime and justice	customs and traditions	daily life
days, months, seasons	education	environmental issues
family and friends	food and drink	geographical features and locations
health and physical feelings	house and home	language learning
leisure interests	the media	parts of the body
personal information	personal possessions	physical appearance
politics, government and society	religion	shops and shopping
social situations	town features and facilities	transport
travel	work	weather

Macmillan Education,
Between Towns Road, Oxford OX4 3PP

A division of Macmillan Publishers Limited

Companies and representatives throughout the world

ISBN 0 435 24217 2

Designed by Giles Davies

Cover designed by Stafford & Stafford
Editorial by Helena Gomm

Illustrated by:
Phil Bannister, p.5, 7, 19, 25, 27
John Batten, p.2, 29, 37, 55
Giles Davies, p.6, 16, 32, 34, 40, 42, 54, 56, 57, 78
Frances Lloyd, p.3 22, 33, 58, 69, 81
Ed McLachlan, p.16, 53, 77
Gillian Martin, p.4, 20, 21, 59
Adrian Salmon, p.42, 73
Judy Stevens, p.38, 44, 45
Gary Wing, p.24, 48, 49

Acknowledgements
The authors would like to thank the following for
permission to reproduce photographic material:
Paul Freestone p 17 (r); Getty Images pp 15 (*lmb. lb*), 75(*tr, bl*);
Pictor p 15 (*lmt*); Rex Features pp 15 (*r*), 24, 75 (*tl, br*); Zefa pp 15
(*tl, mr*), 17 (*l, m*).

While every effort has been made to trace the owners of copyright
material in this book, there have been some cases when the
publishers have been unable to contact the owners. We should be
grateful to hear from anyone who recognises their copyright
material and who is unacknowledged. We shall be pleased to make
the necessary amendments in future editions of the book.

Printed and bound in Great Britain by Martins the Printers Ltd, Berwick upon Tweed

2003 2002
12 11 10 9 8